Great Moments
in Pharmacy

Great Moments in Pharmacy

The stories and paintings in the series

A History of Pharmacy in Pictures

By

PARKE, DAVIS & COMPANY

Stories By

GEORGE A. BENDER

Paintings By

ROBERT A. THOM

DETROIT

NORTHWOOD INSTITUTE PRESS

1966

CONTENTS

PREFACE

*Art and history are the most powerful
instruments of our inquiry into human nature.*

PHARMACY, the profession of the art and science of preparing, preserving, compounding, and dispensing medicines, indeed has a proud heritage—an unequalled record of service to humanity almost as old as the human race itself. This heritage has developed from sincere, careful, indefatigable effort, sometimes right, often wrong, of countless generations of pharmacists, most of whose names are unknown, through fifty centuries of recorded history.

It was to immortalize and to permanently record high lights of these centuries of sincere, dedicated service that the series, *A History of Pharmacy in Pictures*, came into being. By means of original oil paintings and accompanying historical stories, forty milestones along the road of Pharmacy's progress were recorded. Published first in *Modern Pharmacy*, later in other media, the stories on which the paintings are based are reproduced in full in this book.

Thanks are due to many persons in the Parke-Davis organization, in Pharmacy throughout the world, and in related fields, who were sympathetic, encouraging, and helpful to the author and to the artist. Without these, the project might never have been launched; certainly, not completed. The unflagging encouragement, advice, and assistance, as well as unsparing criticism, extended by Dr. George Urdang and Dr. Glenn L. Sonnedecker, of The American Institute of the History of Pharmacy, were of inestimable value. Of particular significance was the happy combination of talents, enthusiasm, perseverence, and personality that Artist Robert A. Thom brought to the team of artist and author—a team able to pursue this task through a decade, and, upon its completion, to begin another of as great proportions— *A History of Medicine in Pictures*.

Detroit, Michigan   GEORGE A. BENDER

BEFORE THE DAWN OF HISTORY

FROM BEGINNINGS both remote and simple came the proud profession of Pharmacy. Its development parallels that of man himself, and its age is but little less than that of the human race.

Ancient man undoubtedly first learned through sheer instinct to assuage his wounds with the materials at hand. When injured because of a fall, a cut, or a wound from a club or stone axe, and blood spurted forth, he instinctively clapped something over the wound to relieve pain and to stanch the flow of vital fluid. It might have been a leaf, cool water, dirt, or mud. By trial, he learned that certain leaves, certain clays, served him better than others. Then, too, he may have observed that birds and animals, when wounded or suffering from broken bones, pack the wound with soothing mud or build crude splints of drying clays. Gradually early man's simple mental processes worked out adaptations of these experiences and observations to meet his own requirements. Still later it occurred to him to apply this knowledge for the benefit of injured members of his family or tribe, for he learned that there was a measure of self-preservation in helping those who were friendly to him to return to usefulness.

Among most primitive people there has been found some crude knowledge of healing, limited though it may be. Before the days of priestcraft, as is pointed out by Thompson, the wise man or woman of the tribe, whose knowledge of the healing properties of herbs and plants had either been gathered from experience or had been handed down by word of mouth from his progenitors, was called on to attend the sick or wounded and prepare the remedy. It was from the methods of preparing the substances thus employed for the treatment of an injury or a disease, either for external or internal use, that the art of the apothecary originated.

Conjecturally, use of crude remedies may have been advanced to this point among the cave dwellers, some four hundred cen-

BEFORE THE DAWN OF HISTORY

From beginnings as remote and as simple as these came the proud profession of Pharmacy. Its development parallels that of man himself. Ancient man learned from instinct, from observation of birds and beasts. Cool water, a leaf, dirt, or mud was his first soothing application. By trial, he learned which served him best. Eventually, he applied his knowledge for the benefit of others. Though the caveman's methods were crude, many of today's medicines spring from sources as simple and elementary as those which were within reach of early man.

turies ago. Relatively advanced on the road of human cultural development, the concept of the worth of tribal preservation and the rudiments of compassion for one's fellows may well have been established in these people. When a member of a tribe (scarcely larger than a family) had been injured, perhaps by an animal, perhaps in an encounter with a hostile neighbor, the more experienced members of the group applied measures known to them—mud from the banks of a nearby stream, and astringent leaves that grew on its banks. Crude though the early applications may have been, clays of various sorts and extracts of leaves still have prominent places in the armamentarium of today's Pharmacy. Indeed, the soil has yielded up many a healing and life-saving substance—for example, organisms from which certain of the highly potent antibiotics have been derived. So the instincts of early forebears of the apothecary were guiding them along a sound pathway.

Recorded history as it pertains to the art of the apothecary takes us back forty to forty-five centuries; but the breadth of the knowledge of drug plants and substances exhibited in these earliest records, while crude according to present standards, had reached a state of understanding and organization that warrants assumption of a background of many centuries of trial, error and triumph. The practice of Pharmacy, like many other cultural and self-preservational devices which man developed, had its birth well before the dawn of history. For many centuries, the beginnings of Pharmacy and Medicine were inextricably interwoven; and at various periods, both were tightly bound in with religious practices. Therefore, the lines of demarcation between the early beginnings of Pharmacy and those of Medicine and Religion are lost in the haze of prehistory.

Certainly the thread of knowledge of drugs and their preparation is woven faintly but firmly into the developmental pattern of mankind from the dawn of understanding; and by the time man first began to record his deeds and thoughts it had developed into a strong cord of experience and understanding which, through existing centuries, has never been sundered.

10

WORLD EVENTS AND PHARMACY HISTORY

The history of Pharmacy and lives of persons who contributed to its advance were influenced by shifting populations, political changes, and social developments.

Dates, persons, and events of significance to the evolution of Pharmacy include:

B. C.

550,000	End of Pliocene Age. First known race of man — *Pithecanthropus erectus.*
110,000	Second race—*Eoanthropus.*
50,000	Third race—*Neanderthal.*
35,000	Beginning of Late Palaeolithic Age. Fourth race—*Cro-Magnon.*
7000-2000	Neolithic Age in Europe.
5000-4500	Dawn of Sumerian, Egyptian, and Minoan cultures.
3400-2500	Old Kingdom: Egypt.
2980	Imhotep.
2900-2625	Age of the pyramid builders.
2500	Surgical operations depicted upon tomb of Pharaohs at Saqquarah.
2445-1731	Middle Kingdom: Egypt.
2000	Code of Hammurabi (Babylon).
2000-1000	Bronze Age in Europe.
1500	Edwin Smith Papyrus. Ebers Papyrus.
1237	Death of Asclepius.
1000-500	Earlier Iron Age in Europe.
950	Homer.
800	Period of Brahminic medicine. Building of Carthage.
753	Founding of Rome.
600	Massage and acupuncture practiced by the Japanese.
580-489	Pythagoras.
550	Buddha, Confucius, Lao Tse lived about this time.
539	Cyrus founded the Persian Empire.
525	Asclepius raised to rank of God of Medicine in Greece.
522	Democedes founded a medical school at Athens.
521	Darius I ruled from the Hellespont to the Indies.
500	Later Iron Age (La Tène culture).
490	Battle of Marathon.
484	Herodotus.
480	Thermopylae and Salamis.
460-361	Hippocrates.
431-404	Peloponnesian War.
429-347	Plato.
384-322	Aristotle.
370-286	Theophrastus of Eresos.
338-323	Alexander the Great.
146	Carthage, Corinth destroyed.
120-63	Mithridates VI.
44	Julius Caesar assassinated.
4	Birth of Jesus of Nazareth.
31 B.C.-14 A.D.	Augustus Caesar.

A. D.

14-37	Tiberius. Celsus.
30	Jesus of Nazareth crucified.
23-79	Pliny the Elder.
54-68	Nero. Dioscorides.
61	Boadicea of Britain massacred by Romans.
79	Plague following eruption of Vesuvius. Pompeii destroyed.
117-138	Hadrian; Roman Empire at height. Aretaeus. Soranus of Ephesus.
130-201	Galen.
161	Marcus Aurelius rules Rome.
220	End of Han Dynasty in China.
303	Martyrdom of Saints Cosmas and Damian.
306	Constantine the Great becomes Emperor of Roman Empire.
369	Hospital of St. Basil erected at Caesarea by Justinian.
395-1453	Byzantine Empire.
400	Fabiola founds first nosocomium (hospital) in Western Europe.
451	Attila raided Gaul.
476	Fall of Western Roman Empire.
527-565	Justinian I. Aëtius of Amida.
528	Monte Cassino founded.
542	Nosocomia founded at Lyons by Childebert I and at Arles by Caesarius.
568-774	Establishment of Lombards in Italy.
571-632	Mohammed.
622	Mohammed's Hegira.
651	Hôtel-Dieu founded by Saint Landry, Bishop of Paris.
711	Moslems invaded Spain from Africa.
749-1258	Eastern Caliphate.
768-814	Charlemagne.
786-802	Reign of Haroun al-Rashid in Bagdad.
820-1517	Rise of Venetian Republic.
848-856	School of Salerno first heard of.
865-925	Rhazes (smallpox and measles).
871-901	Alfred the Great.
980-1036	Avicenna.
1020-1087	Constantinus Africanus.
1066	Battle of Hastings.
1096-1272	Crusades.
1099	Order of St. John of Jerusalem founded.
1110-1113	University of Paris founded.
1126-1198	Averroës, Arab philosopher, in Cordoba. Avenzoar.

PHARMACY IN
ANCIENT BABYLONIA

Mesopotamia, that fertile strip of land between the Tigris and Euphrates rivers, is often credited with being the cradle of civilization. Because of the virtual absence of stone in this region, historical records have been derived largely from the clay tablets on which the ancient peoples of this region, the Babylonians and the Sumerians, recorded their thoughts, deeds and transactions. Fortunately, an abundance of these tablets, rendered almost imperishable by baking, have been discovered and translated. It is from this source that some of the earliest records have been obtained of practices which developed over the centuries into the art and profession of Pharmacy as we know it today.

Medical treatment in Babylonia appears to have been of a primitive type and probably dates from an earlier period than that found in Egypt. In Babylonian medical texts we have the earliest known record of methods employed in preparing medicines, and they comprise the first recorded accounts of the art of the apothecary. There is evidence, too, that, because of its geographical situation, the influence of Babylonia spread to the neighboring countries along the caravan routes to and from India, Arabia, and Egypt.

Early man associated the action of drugs with supernatural forces. To demons and spirits were attributed all the phenomena of nature and the forces which proved to be good or evil in man's daily struggle for existence.

"The art of the apothecary has always been associated with the mysterious," says C. J. S. Thompson, "and its practitioners, owing to their peculiar knowledge of drugs were believed to have connection with the world of spirits . . . So from the wise man of primitive times there developed a special medicine-man of a type found among savage races today. As time went on, this office

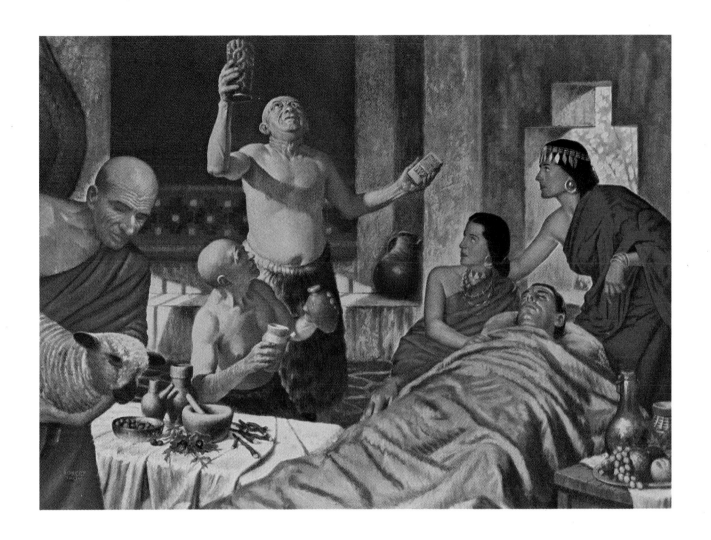

PHARMACY IN ANCIENT BABYLONIA

Babylon, jewel of ancient Mesopotamia, often called the cradle of civilization, provides

the earliest known record of practice of the art of the apothecary. Practitioners of healing

of this era (about 2600 B.C.) were priest, pharmacist and physician, all in one. Medical

texts on clay tablets record first the symptoms of illness, the prescription and directions

for compounding, then an invocation to the gods. Ancient Babylonian methods find

counterpart in today's modern pharmaceutical, medical, and spiritual care of the sick.

became combined with priestly functions, and, among early civilizations, the priest-magician became the healer of the body as well as the soul."

Primary methods of ridding the human body of the demons of disease were incantations and the application or administration of certain herbs, plants or substances. The recital of an incantation may have had some efficacy in soothing patients' nerves; just as today, in certain conditions where drugs are of little value, benefit frequently may be obtained by psychological measures.

From such stock the priest-pharmacist-physician of Babylonia developed. Ancient Babylonian medical texts, recorded on clay tablets, first presented a description of the symptoms, followed by the prescription and directions for compounding, and then an incantation to the gods, says Edward Chiera. The Babylonians were very observant people, and there is no question that the remedies they employed were based on a large body of experience. Among the drug substances which they used were oils of cedar and cypress, myrrh, glycyrrhiza, honey, poppy juice, nutgalls— all of which are still in use. A mixture of olive oil and beer presaged our oil shampoo; and the employment of warm oil for earache dates back to this locale of the ancient world.

In a typical bedside situation, a Babylonian priest-pharmacist-physician might have been found alternately offering incantations to the gods in behalf of the ill patient, and instructions to an assistant for compounding a remedy. Directions for both were set forth upon clay tablets which he would have consulted. A priest assistant would have brought in a lamb, which would have been placed beside the patient. If the treatment was successful, the demons of disease supposedly would have been driven from the body of the patient to the animal; and the lamb later would have been sacrificed and studied for evidence to determine whether this desired result had been accomplished.

Crude though they may seem, these practices are not without their modern counterpart. We look upon incantations with derision; but today we call upon the physician to diagnose and prescribe; the pharmacist to compound and dispense; the clergy to pray for our sick. We want our science and our religion unmixed. In ancient civilizations one person sometimes attended to all three. For the magic and sorcery of old we have substituted the comforting psychology of the physician's bedside manner.

As to the demon-baiting sacrificial lamb, Chiera points out that "we have reversed the process and improved on it. We take an animal and pass into it the disease of a man, then we take part of this animal and pass it into a diseased man to effect a cure, or into a well man to prevent the disease from attacking him." The products of this practice are in familiar packages in every pharmacy's biological department. Perhaps the ancient Babylonian prototype of the apothecary was closer to the goal of rationality than he is generally credited with being.

The mute clay tablets record professional practices of men long dead; but the early Babylonian science of drugs, their preparation and combination, spread far from the Tigris and Euphrates basins, and influenced Pharmacy's beginnings for many centuries.

PHARMACY IN ANCIENT CHINA

OF THREE legendary Chinese figures who are supposed to have lived between 3000 and 2200 B.C., and who are regarded as the founders of Chinese Pharmacy and Medicine, Shen Nung, also known as the Blazing Emperor, is most repeatedly and persistently recorded as the first to have sought out and investigated the medicinal values of herbs. Though some historians place his period as 2838 to 2698 B.C., later researchers question whether the prehistoric period just prior to 1700 B.C. is not more plausible.

Shen Nung, according to Hume, "determined to search for remedies, particularly among the herbs of the soil," when his people suffered from sickness. "So ceaselessly did he pursue the quest that it became a universal saying, 'Shen Nung daily tested a hundred herbs.'" He is credited with having tested their effects on himself, and with having laid the foundations of the pharmacopoeia which has been China's proud possession for the last 3000 years. Shen Nung, who examined many plants brought from the fields, also is credited with having "engaged in domestic improvements, examined the quality of the soil, and the character of the climate, made plows, and taught his people how to till the soil . . ." The mathematical design, the *Pa Kua*, which was closely associated with the healing arts, is said to have come down from Shen Nung's predecessor, Fu Hsi. The *Pa Kua*, or eight diagrams, had for its center the symbol of creation, and is said to be "the predecessor of mathematics and of written characters."

Wong and Wu also frequently mention Shen Nung. The people of his day dressed in skins and leaves; they were not too far advanced in the arts. Among the drugs Shen Nung is reputed to have discovered is *Ma Huang*, or Ephedra—a bamboo-like grass. This ancient Chinese herb, for many years disregarded in medical circles, became important again early in the twentieth century when research revealed its content of the important drug, ephedrine. Conceivably Shen Nung also may have known and tested such ancient drugs as cinnamon, datura alba, aconite, rhubarb,

PHARMACY IN ANCIENT CHINA

Chinese Pharmacy, according to legend, stems from Shen Nung (about 2000 B.C.), emperor who sought out and investigated the medicinal value of several hundred herbs. He is reputed to have tested many of them on himself, and to have written the first Pen T'sao, *or native herbal, recording 365 drugs. Still worshiped by native Chinese drug guilds as their patron god, Shen Nung conceivably examined many herbs, barks, and roots brought in from the fields, swamps, and woods that are still recognized in Pharmacy today. In the background is the "Pa Kua," a mathematical design symbolizing creation and life. Medicinal plants include podophyllum, rhubarb, ginseng, stramonium, cinnamon bark, and, in the boy's hand, ma huang, or Ephedra.*

and others which have figured in Chinese Pharmacy since history has been recorded.

According to legends related by Wong and Wu, Shen Nung "is said to have tested 70 different kinds of poisons in a single day." Tradition ascribes to him the writing of the first *Pen T'sao*, or native herbal. The volume is said to contain 365 drugs, which Shen Nung classified as superior, medium and inferior in quality with regard to the treatment of disease. This authorship is questioned by some authorities, who state that the book could not have been written until many centuries later; but it is believed that the later books were accumulations of information, the organization of which began with Shen Nung. He is a symbol of belief in empirical knowledge, which has been so characteristic an aspect of China's pharmaceutical practice through the ages.

Chinese medicine, according to Hume, teaches that health and disease are due to the balance and imbalance of living forces, acting alike on man and animals. Since drugs, like everything else in nature, were considered by the early Chinese to be animated, they too were considered to carry helpful or malicious spirits; and, in addition to pharmacological action, their shape, in relation to the human body or its organs, also was considered important. It is not unlikely, therefore, that mandrake and ginseng, two drugs still revered by Chinese when their root shapes simulate the form of the human body, also may have been attributed healing virtues by Shen Nung, who is worshiped even today by native drug guilds as their patron god. Though modern practices gain headway, Chinese reverence for ancient ways is still strong.

WORLD EVENTS AND PHARMACY HISTORY

Dates, persons, and events of significance to the evolution of Pharmacy include:

1131	Council of Rheims forbid clerics to practice medicine.
1135-1204	Moses Maimonides.
1137	St. Bartholomew's Hospital (London) founded by Rahere.
1140	King Roger II of Sicily restricted medical practice to licentiates.
1158	University of Bologna founded.
1180	University of Montpellier founded.
1198	Frederick II (aged 4) became King of Sicily.
1193-1280	Albertus Magnus.
1198	Hospital movement inaugurated by Innocent III.
1201	Oxford first called a university.
1204	Innocent III opened Santo Spirito in Sassia Hospital (Rome).
1210	Collège de St. Come founded at Paris by Jean Pitard.
1211	Innocent III recognized University of Paris.
1212	Children's Crusade.
1214-1294	Roger Bacon.
1215	Magna Charta signed in Britain.
1215	St. Thomas's Hospital founded.
1222	University of Padua started.
1223	Cambridge became a university.
1227-1274	Thomas Aquinas.
1231	Medical school at Salerno.
1235-1311	Arnold of Villanova.
1240	Law of Frederick II favoring dissection and regulating practice of medicine and pharmacy.
1244-1245	University of Oxford chartered.
1246-1248	University of Siena started.
1252-1517	Mameluke Dynasties (Egypt).
1257	Sorbonne founded at Paris.
1260-1320	Henri de Mondeville.
1266	End of Western Caliphate.
1270-1280	Spectacles introduced by Venetians.
1271	Marco Polo began travels.
1280	Kublai Khan founded Yuan (Mongol) Dynasty in China.
1300-1368	Guy de Chauliac.
1303	Universities of Rome chartered.
1319	First criminal prosecution for body snatching.
1330	Gunpowder used in warfare.
1336-1453	Hundred Years' War.
1345	First apothecary shop in London.
1347	University of Prague chartered.
1348	Gonville and Caius College (University of Cambridge) founded.
1348-1350	Black Death (magna mortalitas).
1368	Ming Dynasty succeeds Yuan Dynasty in China.

1376	Board of medical examiners in London.
1385	University of Heidelberg chartered.
1402	University of Würzburg chartered.
1429-1431	Syphilis first mentioned.
1440-1450	Invention of printing.
1443	Hôtel-Dieu de Beaune, France, founded.
1452-1519	Leonardo da Vinci.
1454	Gutenberg Bible printed.
1457	Gutenberg Purgation-Calendar (first medical publication).
1477	Universities of Tübingen and Upsala founded.
1478	Spanish Inquisition.
1479	First edition of Avicenna printed.
1490-1553	Rabelais.
1492	Discovery of America by Columbus.
1493-1541	Paracelsus.
1497	Scurvy on Vasco da Gama's voyage.
1498	Florentine *Receptario* (first official pharmacopoeia).
1505	Royal College of Surgeons of Edinburgh chartered.
1505	University of Seville chartered.
1509-1547	Reign of Henry VIII in England.
1510-1590	Ambroise Paré.
1514-1564	Andreas Vesalius.
1517	Luther propounded his theses at Wittenberg.
1518	Royal College of Physicians (England) founded (September 23).
1519-1556	Charles V, King of Spain and Emperor of Germany.
1524	Cortes erected hospital in Mexico.
1526	Paracelsus founded chemotherapy.
1530	Collège de France (Paris) founded.
1536	Paracelsus' *Chirurgia Magna* published.
1538	Vesalius published his *Tabulae Anatomicae Sex.*
1538	University of Santo Tomas (San Domingo) founded.
1540	English barbers and surgeons united as "Commonalty of the Barbers and Surgeons."
1540	Valerius Cordus discovered sulfuric ether.
1543	Copernicus described revolution of planets around the sun (1507).
1543	Vesalius published the *Fabrica*.
1543	English apothecaries legalized by Act of Parliament.
1544	Albert III founded University of Königsberg (August 17).

DAYS OF THE PAPYRUS EBERS

THE MATERIA MEDICA of the ancient Egyptians was very rich, and their pharmaceutical activities skilfully executed. Legends indicate that Egyptian medicine got its start with Imhotep, architect and possibly physician to the court of King Zoser, about 2900 B.C. (roughly contemporary with the Chinese, Shen Nung), but accurate records of medical practices have not been found dating earlier than 1900 B.C.

Among the mythological deities who were supposed to have special concern for Pharmacy were Thoth, Osiris, Isis and Horus. Imhotep, who was a real personage and lived about 3000 B.C., was not deified until 2500 years after his death. Therefore, Anepu, whom the Greeks called Anubis, most likely would have been the prevailing deity concerned with the practice of Pharmacy, about 1500 B.C., approximate date of the *Papyrus Ebers*.

There are, according to Urdang, eight so-called medical papyri unearthed in Egypt which have thus far been translated, all written sometime between 1900 and 1100 B.C. Best known and most important so far as Pharmacy is concerned is the *Papyrus Ebers*. It is supposed to have been written about 1500 B.C.

The *Papyrus Ebers* might be considered a sort of formulary, or collection of various prescriptions. It contains 811 prescriptions, and mentions 700 drugs of mineral, vegetable, and animal origin. There are formulas for gargles, snuffs, inhalations, suppositories, fumigations, enemas, poultices, decoctions, infusions, pills, troches, lotions, ointments, and plasters. Beer, milk, wine, and honey are common vehicles for most of the compounded drugs.

Von Klein states that "A large portion of the diseases known to modern medical science are carefully described and their symptoms classified." Indication that the Egyptian pharmacist was aware of cosmetic needs, too, may be realized from the seventy-four prescriptions that pertain to hair washes, dyes, oils and

DAYS OF THE PAPYRUS EBERS

Though Egyptian medicine dates from about 2900 B.C., best known and most important pharmaceutical record is the "Papyrus Ebers" (1500 B.C.), a collection of 800 prescriptions, mentioning 700 drugs. Pharmacy in ancient Egypt was conducted by two or more echelons: gatherers and preparers of drugs, and "chiefs of fabrication," or head pharmacists. They are thought to have worked in the "House of Life." In a setting such as this, the "Papyrus Ebers" might have been dictated to a scribe by a head pharmacist as he directed compounding activities in the drug room.

depilatories. Urdang presents interesting side lights on the drugs (many still in use) and pharmaceutical processes described in the *Papyrus Ebers* in his *History of Pharmacy*.

According to Grapow, ancient Egyptian medicine, revealing a scientific character, reached its full development before 1600 B.C., but later, in the time of the New Kingdom, it degenerated into sorcery. Many of the recipes in the *Papyrus Ebers* are supposed to have come down from a period of remote antiquity. The exact date and authorship of the papyrus are unknown.

One has to keep in mind that the *Papyrus Ebers*, like all ancient manuscripts still in existence, is not an original, but, to quote H. E. Sigerist's *A History of Medicine*, is "a copy or copies with all the mistakes and changes, additions and omissions, that a tradition of many centuries necessarily involves."

Of the pharmacists of this period, Schelenz reports that "The profession had a high repute; the priestly physician-pharmacist himself was venerable." Urdang stated that "A special room in the temple, the *asi-t*, was provided for his work." Here, seemingly, he would have had many helpers. However, the eminent Egyptologist, Frans Jonckheere, disagrees, claiming that there is no evidence of a connection between the priesthood and the practice of pharmacy.

In early Egypt, the personnel of Pharmacy apparently included at least two echelons: a group of specialists, or "chief preparers of drugs;" and a complex of technical people, who ranked below the first category. Since Egyptian pharmacy and medicine employed vegetable products from widely separated areas, some of them from outside Egypt, there is indication of a class of herbalists, or drug-gatherers. Egyptians were great travelers, and were aware of developments of their time in other parts of the world. Also, there appears to have been individuals known as "conservators of drugs," responsible for proper storage of medicinal substances.

While there is evidence indicating that some physicians also prepared their own medicines, Jonckheere indicates that there were Egyptian functionaries designated as "those who fabricate the medicaments," and an official designated as "chief of those who fabricate the medicaments," quite distinct from those having medical responsibilities. In the "House of Life" (perhaps a medical training center, at Sais), it appears that drugs were not only collected and stored, but also were prepared for use as medicines.

In a surrounding such as the House of Life, perhaps, some Egyptian chief pharmacist might have set down for posterity the pharmaceutical and medical knowledge of his day. Conceivably, he might have dictated the notes to a scribe, while directing the compounding work of his assistants. By a lucky set of circumstances the record was preserved, and through discovery by George Ebers, in 1875, the papyrus is available to Egyptologists today for intensive study.

THEOPHRASTUS
FATHER OF BOTANY

CALLED "the father of botany," and perhaps entitled to be called "the father of pharmacognosy," Theophrastus of Eresus was a close associate of the greatest among the great early Greek philosophers and natural scientists, Aristotle, and his successor as leader of the peripatetic school in Athens. This group had no fixed meeting place, but moved about in search of knowledge and held discussions when and where it was convenient at the moment.

Theophrastus was recognized for his extraordinary gift of oratory, and for his extensive observations on all types of subjects. Of his writings that were preserved and have come down to us, his botanical works are the most substantial and important.

The recognition accorded Theophrastus as "the father of botany" does not mean that there were no scientific writers on the subject before him. However, the completeness of his work, as it has come down to us, leaves little doubt that he was the one who most definitely and systematically fought the superstitious ideas and dogmatism that were rife in his time, replacing them in his writings on botanical and other subjects with his own observations and logical inferences. Thus the scientific observer began to take the place of, or to question the infallibility of, the school of philosophers whose utterances were based upon purely speculative or theoretical musings. In his metaphysical essays, Theophrastus shows a hesitant and questioning attitude, according to Cohen and Drabkin. "A good deal of the material in his botanical works consists of minute and accurate descriptions quite independent of metaphysical considerations. Thus, he prefers to begin the *History of Plants* with a description of what constitutes a plant."

It is in the ninth book of his *History of Plants* that Theophrastus deals especially with the medical qualities and peculiarities of

THEOPHRASTUS — FATHER OF BOTANY

Theophrastus (about 300 B.C.), among the greatest early Greek philosophers and natural scientists, is called "the father of botany." His observations and writings dealing with the medical qualities and peculiarities of herbs are unusually accurate, even in the light of present knowledge. He lectured to informal groups of students who walked about with him, learning of nature by observing her treasures at first-hand. In his hand he holds a branch of belladonna. Behind him are pomegranate blooms, senna, and manuscript scrolls. Slabs of ivory, coated with colored bees-wax, served students as "slates." Writing was cut into the surface with a stylus.

herbs. His contributions to Pharmacy stem not only from these observations, which form a basic structure for pharmacognosy, but also from special chapters in which, with his unusually keen and orderly methods of observation and writing, he describes the preparation and uses of drugs obtained from plant sources. His pharmaceutical and pharmacological observations are unusually accurate, even in the light of present-day knowledge. He is, to our knowledge, the first to have mentioned *filix* (the fern) and its effect; and incense, myrrh, and cassia are described by him in detail. In his treatise *On Odors*, he describes the water bath and its uses in detail.

Theophrastus also knew of and made use of the ability to change the character of plants by cultivation, transforming, for instance, wild mint (*menthrastrum*) to tame mint (*mentha*). In addition to those previously mentioned, Theophrastus undoubtedly was familiar with such drugs as peppermint, frankincense, laurel, *Iris florentinus*, figs, thyme, *Juniperus communis*, fennel, *Atropa belladonna*, black pepper, and squill. Theophrastus also is known to have utilized *in his botanical work* the writings of scientists who accompanied Alexander the Great on the famous conquest of the Asiatic world. His students took notes on the "granddaddy" of the slate —slightly depressed slabs of ivory over which colored beeswax was flowed. Writing was done by cutting through the wax with a stylus.

Beside laying the groundwork for scientific botany on the whole, Theophrastus immortalized himself to Pharmacy through having contributed many observations to pharmacology and pharmacognosy proper; and, most important, for having put these sciences on a rational basis. It was one of his great merits that he based much of his botanical writings on firsthand observation—what we would today call "field work."

WORLD EVENTS AND PHARMACY HISTORY

Dates, persons, and events of significance to the evolution of Pharmacy include:

1545	Giambattista da Monte gave bedside instruction at Padua.
1549	Anatomical theater at Padua.
1550	Paré's essay on podalic version published.
1558-1603	Reign of Elizabeth I.
1561	Fallopius published *Observationes Anatomicae* (fallopian tubes).
1561-1626	Francis Bacon.
1564-1616	Shakespeare.
1564-1642	Galileo.
1578-1657	William Harvey.
1582	University of Edinburgh chartered.
1584	Sir Walter Raleigh brought curare from Guiana and introduced the potato.
1590	Compound microscope invented by Hans and Zacharias Janssen.
1599-1660	Velasquez.
1604-1609	Galileo elucidates law of falling bodies.
1606-1669	Rembrandt.
1607	Settlement of Jamestown, Virginia.
1609	United Netherlands.
1609	Henry Hudson anchors "Half Moon" in New York Bay.
1609	Galileo invented telescope.
1609-1618	Kepler stated laws of planetary motion.
1610	Galileo devised microscope.
1611	University of Santo Tomas (Manila) founded.
1613	University of Cordova (Argentina) founded.
1615-1616	Harvey lectured on the circulation of the blood.
1617	Guild of Apothecaries of the City of London founded.
1618	First edition of *London Pharmacopoeia*.
1618-1648	Thirty Years' War.
1620	Landing of the Pilgrims at Plymouth, Massachusetts.
1620	Van Helmont stressed chemical role of gastric juice in digestion.
1622-1673	Molière.
1624-1689	Thomas Sydenham.
1628	Harvey published *De Motu Cordis*.
1630-1638	Treatment of malarial fever with cinchona bark known in Peru.
1632-1723	Antony van Leeuwenhoek.
1636	Harvard College founded.
1639	First hospital in Canada.
1639-1650	Juan del Vigo introduced cinchona into Spain and Italy.
1643	Sir Edward Greaves described typhus fever as a "new disease" in England.

1644	Hôtel Dieu in Montreal.
1645	Royal ("Invisible") Society founded in London.
1648	Van Helmont's *Ortus Medicinae* published.
1648	Francesco Redi disproved theory of spontaneous generation.
1649-1660	Commonwealth in England.
1654-1715	Reign of Louis XIV.
1660	Willis described puerperal fever.
1661	Malpighi published first account of capillary system (*De pulmonibus*).
1661	Robert Boyle defined chemical elements and isolated acetone.
1661	Descartes published first treatise on physiology (*De homine*).
1661	De Graaf showed that ova arise in the ovary.
1665	Newton discovered binomial theorem (published 1669) and law of gravitation.
1665	Great Plague of London.
1666	Great Fire of London.
1669	Lower showed that venous blood takes up air in the lungs.
1670	Malpighi discovered malpighian bodies in spleen and kidneys.
1670	Willis discovered sweet taste of diabetic urine.
1672	Le Gras brought ipecac to Europe from America (Piso, 1648).
1672	De Graaf described the graafian follicles in the ovary.
1673	Leeuwenhoek began making microscopes.
1675	Leeuwenhoek discovered protozoa.
1681	Royal College of Physicians of Edinburgh founded.
1682-1725	Peter the Great ruled Russia.
1682-1771	Giovanni Battista Morgagni.
1683	Sydenham's treatise on gout published.
1683	Leeuwenhoek described and sketched bacteria.
1685-1750	Johann Sebastian Bach.
1690	Locke's "Essay Concerning Human Understanding" published.
1693	College of William and Mary founded, Williamsburg, Va.
1698	Statute of Montpellier required students to visit hospitals.
1702	Stahl stated phlogiston theory.
1708-1777	Haller.
1710	Charité Hospital opened at Berlin.
1713	St. Côme merged into Académie de Chirurgie (Paris).

THE ROYAL TOXICOLOGIST
MITHRIDATES VI

FROM men's fears, their cupidity, and from the drives of their ambitions have come many of the beginnings of scientific advances —and Pharmacy and Medicine have profited as have their sister sciences from the works of investigators about whose motives there may hang a cloud of dubiety.

Mithridates VI, King of Pontus from about 120 to 63 B.C., whom history called "the Great" because of his powerful personality and his valiant, lifelong fight against Rome, was an early representative of royalty dabbling in Medicine and Pharmacy. An Asiatic prince, whose Greek education and mastery of 22 languages ingratiated him with the nations in Asia Minor which became his allies against the military might of Rome, Mithridates lived in a world in which murder was a common and almost an accepted political device. Mithridates frequently employed, and at the same time very much feared, assassination. Despite his surface gloss of Greek education, he embodied the subtlety, the superstition, the unreasoning suspicion and obstinate endurance of an Oriental of his time.

It was especially murder through poisoning that was in vogue at royal courts through the ages. Mithridates is said to have been one of the first, if not the first, who made not only the art of poisoning, but also the art of preventing and counteracting poisoning, subjects of intensive study by himself as well as by scientists in his pay. Among them were the famous "rhizotomists" (plant scientists as well as plant gatherers). Hence, it can be said with some justification that the science of toxicology had in Mithridates one of its early promoters.

Victorious and defeated in breath-taking changes throughout his 57-year reign, Mithridates and his life became subject to legend

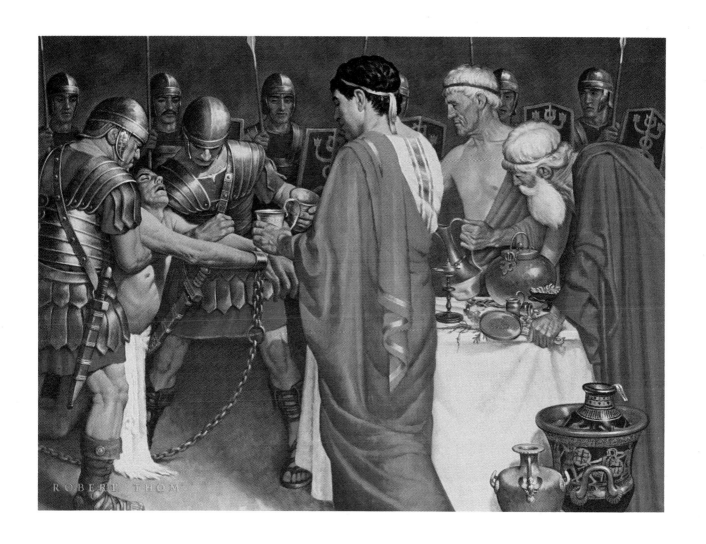

THE ROYAL TOXICOLOGIST—MITHRIDATES VI

Mithridates VI, King of Pontus (about 100 B.C.), though he battled Rome for a lifetime, found time to make not only the art of poisoning, but also the art of preventing and counteracting poisoning, subjects of intensive study. Unhesitatingly, he used himself as well as his prisoners as "guinea pigs" on which to test poisons and antidotes. Behind him are rhizotomists, offering fresh, flowering aconite, ginger, and gentian. At lower right is a crater—a two-piece forerunner of the champagne bucket. His famed formula of alleged panantidotal powers, "Mithridatum," was popular for over a thousand years.

among the peoples of the East and even among the Greeks and Romans. He trusted no one; yet, admiring the military abilities of his most bitter adversaries, the Romans, Mithridates armed and outfitted his troops after the Roman fashion.

"The fable of his medicinal secrets took possession of the imagination of the Romans," says A. C. Wootton in *Chronicles of Pharmacy*. "They were especially attracted by the stories of his famous antidote. According to some he invented this himself; others say the secret was communicated to him by a Persian physician named Zophyrus . . . When the Roman general, Pompey, had finally defeated Mithridates, he took possession of a quantity of the tyrant's papers at Nicopolis, and it was reported that among these were medicinal formulas. Mithridates meanwhile was seeking help to further prosecute the war, but his allies, his own son, and his soldiers were all tired of him. In his despair he poisoned his wives and daughters, and then took poison himself. But according to the legend, propagated perhaps by some clever quacks in Rome, he had so successfully immunized his body to the effects of all poisons that they would now take no effect. Consequently he had to call for the assistance of a Gallic soldier, who despatched his chief with a spear."

A formula alleged to have been found by Pompey among the possessions of Mithridates gradually gained a reputation as an antidote against all kinds of poisons, and later as a cure-all. It was called *Mithridatum*—thus carrying the name of this royal dabbler through pharmaceutical literature for more than a thousand years after his death. Various kinds of theriaca later found places beside (or as substitutes for) *Mithridatum*, but they were modifications of the original product.

Whether the historic formula for *Mithridatum* which Pompey found was true or spurious, it was a very simple one, and in the light of today's knowledge, without imaginable antipoisonous effect. Its reputation was great, however; and the most important modification made in *Mithridatum* was during the first century A.D. by the physician to the Roman Emperor, Nero Andromachus, who added vipers and increased the portion of opium. In this form the compound was emphatically approved by Galen and became the model of the class of compounds known as theriaca in later pharmaceutical literature. Even today, there are advocates of mixtures no less complex than those compounded by Mithridates.

WORLD EVENTS AND PHARMACY HISTORY

Dates, persons, and events of significance to the evolution of Pharmacy include:

1714-1715	Timoni and Pylarini communicated Asiatic practice of smallpox inoculation to Royal Society.
1716-1794	James Lind.
1718	Lady Mary Wortley Montagu had son inoculated for smallpox.
1718	Geoffroy published table of chemical relationships.
1719	Neumann reported thymol.
1721	Zabdiel Boylston inoculated for smallpox in Boston (June 26).
1722-1809	Leopold Auenbrugger.
1728-1793	John Hunter.
1730	Frobenius described preparation of sulfuric ether.
1740	University of Pennsylvania founded as "College of Philadelphia."
1740	Maria Theresa began reign in Austria.
1740	Thomas Dover invented "Dover's Powder."
1740-1786	Reign of Frederick the Great.
1743	Red Cross arrangement at Battle of Dettingen (June 27).
1743-1794	Antoine Laurent Lavoisier.
1745-1813	Benjamin Rush.
1745-1826	Philippe Pinel.
1746	College of New Jersey (Princeton University) founded.

1747	Marggraf discovered sugar in the sugar beet.
1749-1823	Edward Jenner.
1750	Griffith Hughes gave classic account of yellow fever of 1715 (Barbados).
1751	Pennsylvania Hospital founded at Philadelphia.
1752	Smellie's *Midwifery* published.
1752	Medical Society founded in London.
1752	St. George's Hospital (London) founded.
1753	Lind's *A Treatise on Scurvy* published.
1754	King's College (Columbia University) founded at New York.
1754-1757	Black discovered carbon dioxide.
1761	Morgagni's *De sedibus* published.
1761	Auenbrugger's *Inventum novum* published.
1765	Medical Department of University of Pennsylvania founded.
1767	Kay and Hargreaves invented spinning jenny (beginning of Industrial Revolution in England).
1768	Baumé created the hydrometer.
1768	Marggraf discovered hydrogen fluoride.
1769	Guy's Hospital (London) founded.

TERRA SIGILLATA—AN EARLY "TRADEMARKED" DRUG

THE PRACTICE of "trademarking" drug preparations, thus identifying them as the products of certain specific producers or places, became a part of the pharmaceutical art well before the Christian era. Men learned early the prestigious advantage of such warranties as a means of gaining customers' confidence, and the commercial advantage of an easily recognized mark. Thus, the trademark, as applied to drugs and medicines, is no invention of modern times.

One of the first-recognized therapeutic agents to which such an identifying mark was applied was *Terra Sigillata* (Sealed Earth), a clay tablet originating on a Mediterranean island near the shores of Asia Minor.

Earth, the soil on which man was born, lived, and died, has been used by him as medicine, internally as well as externally, from the earliest days of recorded history. Mystical concepts and empirical experience contributed to the belief in the healing powers of earth. It was on the basis of selective experience that, as far as internal use was concerned, gradually a special kind of earth, a rather fatty clay containing silica, aluminum, chalk, magnesia, and traces of oxide of iron, gained fame in these ancient days as a drug of choice.

From a modern point of view, the ingredients mentioned indicate that this clay might be expected to act as an adsorbent; hence, it might well have been useful against diarrhea, and as an antacid. In early days, and even up to the early nineteenth century, *Terra Sigillata* was used as an antidote for poisons as well as in treatment of dysenteries, internal ulcers, hemorrhages, gonorrhea,

TERRA SIGILLATA—AN EARLY "TRADEMARKED" DRUG

Man learned early of the prestigious advantage of trademarks as a means of identification of source and of gaining customers' confidence. One of the first therapeutic agents to bear such a mark was Terra Sigillata (*Sealed Earth*), *a clay tablet originating on the Mediterranean island of Lemnos before 500 B.C. One day each year clay was dug from a pit on a Lemnian hillside in the presence of governmental and religious dignitaries. Washed, refined, rolled to a mass of proper thickness, the clay was formed into pastilles and impressed with an official seal by priestesses, then sun-dried. The tablets were then widely distributed commercially.*

33

pestilential fevers, complaints of the kidneys, and of eye infections. While many of these powers undoubtedly were imaginary, *Terra Sigillata* had enough simple virtues to persist in pharmaceutical literature for some two thousand years. Its modern counterparts, kaolin, bentonite, and compounds of magnesium, aluminum, and silicon, are not lightly regarded in twentieth-century pharmacopoeias.

Most striking feature of this drug, however, was the way in which it was marketed, and the method of identifying it and warranting its origin from a definite source.

The first clay thus marketed had been taken, at least since the time of Herodotus (5th century, B.C.), from a pit on a desolate hill on the Island of Lemnos. The clay was dug, carried to the nearby village, washed, formed into pastilles and impressed while still soft with a significant seal. The first seal used is said to have been in the form of a goat. Later, the head of the Goddess Diana was used. Still later, the head of the Saviour was reproduced; and following conquest of Lemnos by the Turks, the Turkish crescent moon, sometimes accompanied by a star, or a goat, was stamped on the Lemnian earth. The lozenges of Sealed Earth were distributed by various means and sold as medicine throughout all parts of the known world.

The digging traditionally took place on only one day of the year, with considerable ceremony and in the presence of the principal inhabitants of the island. Originally the ceremony was associated with the worship of Diana, and the date of the performance was the sixth of May. In Christian times the day fixed was the sixth of August, according to the Greek church calendar the "Fete of the Saviour." Dioscorides, first century A.D., and one century later, Galen, recommended Lemnian earth highly, the latter denying the story reported by the former that the earth of Lemnos was mixed with goat's blood before being formed into pastilles.

In classical Greece the main competition for Lemnian earth came from the Island of Samos. The great demand for *Terra Sigillata* and the good business that the sale of these troches brought caused people in almost every country in Europe to look for similar earths.

At the end of the seventeenth century there was a great variety of white, red and yellow sealed earths on the market showing different impressions—the images of saints, ships, plants, coats of arms, and the like.

Of no little significance, however, is this early—perhaps first—application of the device now known as the trademark to a drug product. This practice, commonly recognized today as a means of protecting the rights and interests of both the buyer and the seller, has behind it the sanction and approval of some 2500 years of man's experience in world commerce.

WORLD EVENTS AND PHARMACY HISTORY

Dates, persons, and events of significance to the evolution of Pharmacy include:

1769	Napoleon Bonaparte born.
1769	Scheele discovered tartaric acid.
1770	William Hunter founded school of anatomy in London.
1770	First medical degree in United States conferred upon Robert Tucker by King's College.
1770-1827	Beethoven.
1771-1774	Priestley and Scheele isolated oxygen ("dephlogisticated air").
1771-1830	Ephraim McDowell.
1772	Beginnings of modern Japanese medicine.
1772	Priestley discovered nitrogen and nitrous oxide.
1773	Medical Society of London founded.
1773	Rouelle discovered urea.
1774	Scheele discovered chlorine.
1774	Wiegleb discovered myristic acid.
1774	Rouelle defined chemical nature of a salt.
1775	Lavoisier isolated and defined oxygen; also defined an acid.
1775	Andrew Craigie became first Apothecary General in America.
1775	John Morgan appointed Medical Director General of American Army.
1775-1783	American Revolution.

1776	Declaration of Independence of the United States of America.
1777	Lavoisier described exchange of gases in respiration.
1777	Scheele's experiments with silver chloride laid groundwork for photography.
1778	William Brown published first American pharmacopoeia.
1779	Pott described deformity and paralysis from spinal caries.
1779	Mesmer's memoir of animal magnetism published.
1779	Hôpital Necker (Paris) founded.
1780	Benjamin Franklin invented bifocal lenses.
1781-1826	René Théophile Hyacinthe Laennec.
1782	Medical Department of Harvard University founded.
1783	Scheele discovered glycerin.
1783	DeRozier made first balloon ascension.
1783-1785	Lavoisier decomposed water and overthrew phlogiston theory.
1784	Allgemeines Krankenhaus opened at Vienna (August 16).
1784	King's College (New York) rechartered as Columbia College.
1784	Scheele discovered citric acid.

DIOSCORIDES—A SCIENTIST
LOOKS AT DRUGS

THERE COMES a time in the evolution of all successful and
enduring systems of knowledge when the scattered observations of
many men, or the intensive studies of one, transcend from the level
of trade or vocation to that of a science. To such a transition in
Pharmacy, Pedanios Dioscorides contributed mightily.

The exact dates of Dioscorides' birth and death are not known,
but he was born at Anazarbos in that part of Asia Minor which was
entirely graecized and was then a part of the Roman Empire.

In order to study the materia medica of the then known world,
Dioscorides accompanied Roman armies throughout Asia Minor,
and traveled in Italy, Greece, Gaul, and Spain. Of a keenly
scientific turn of mind, he recorded what he observed, as he
observed it, without compromise with or deference to the persistent
myths and wrong guesses of the day. Out of his travels came the
book that made him famous, which was written about the year
77 A.D.

Of the writings of Dioscorides, the highly critical Galen, who
lived a century later, stated that "in his *De materia medica libri
quinque*, the Anazarbean Dioscorides has written in a useful way on
the entire materia medica because he not only deals with the herbs,
but includes the trees, fruits, seeds, the natural and artificial juices
and furthermore the metals and animal substances. In my opinion,
he is the one among the various authors who has presented the most
perfect discussion of the drugs." Galen's word was dogma for
fifteen centuries.

Alexander Tschirch in his *Handbuch der Pharmacognosie* character-
izes the work of Dioscorides as follows:

"Dioscorides was undoubtedly the most important representative
of the science of drugs in antiquity. Until his sources and precursors
were known he appeared so totally unique that one can easily

DIOSCORIDES — A SCIENTIST LOOKS AT DRUGS

In the evolution of all successful and enduring systems of knowledge there comes a time when the observations of many men, or the intensive studies of one, transcend from the level of trade or vocation to that of a science. Pedanios Dioscorides (first century A.D.), contributed mightily to such a transition in Pharmacy. In order to study materia medica, Dioscorides accompanied the Roman armies throughout the known world. He recorded what he observed, promulgated excellent rules for the collection of drugs, their storage and use. His texts were considered basic science as late as the sixteenth century.

conceive why he and almost only he was paid the highest respect in the field of the science of drugs, not only in his time but long afterwards. But still now, knowing his sources at least partly, and sometimes even because of this knowledge, we look at Dioscorides as the greatest of all the men concerned and as a genuine natural scientist who observes and who examines the reports conveyed to him. Thinking, for instance, of the fanciful stories about plants which were printed and believed still in the seventeenth century, Dioscorides appears indeed as a very rare individual, as a really outstanding person. One understands that it was difficult to overcome the influence of such a man at the beginning of modern times, just as it was difficult to overcome the authority of Aristotle . . .

"Through the fact that he described exactly the drugs from the vegetable, the animal and the mineral kingdoms, and, for the purpose of scientific knowledge, arranged his descriptions methodically, Dioscorides became the accepted teacher of pharmacognosy. His great work is the most important source concerning the drugs known in antiquity. Still in the sixteenth century, i.e., after a millennium and a half, it was the oracle of the science of drugs, the bible of the pharmacologists and the last court of appeal as to the identification of medicinal plants." Dioscorides also knew of the formation of lead plaster from fats and lead oxide.

The book of Dioscorides saw a revival through a commented upon and enlarged edition by the Italian physician Peter Andreas Mattioli (1501-1577). It appeared for the first time, in Latin, in 1554. This was followed by not less than 40 further editions and translations, quite a number of which became popular herbals.

Excellent rules for the collection of drugs were promulgated by Dioscorides. He explained the usual adulterations, and suggested means for discovering them. He also recorded most adequate and detailed rules for the storage of various types of drugs. In him, indeed, Pharmacy found a true friend and scientist, whose contributions to its fund of knowledge were both well organized and sound. In turn, his work helped the public by speeding the evolutionary processes of early medicine.

WORLD EVENTS AND PHARMACY HISTORY

Dates, persons, and events of significance to the evolution of Pharmacy include:

1785-1853	William Beaumont.
1785	Cod liver oil first used by English physicians.
1785	Lowitz announced decolorizing, deodorizing properties of charcoal.
1785	Minkelers first used illuminating gas in balloons.
1785	Withering's treatise on the foxglove (digitalis) published.
1785	Scheele discovered malic acid.
1789	Klaproth discovered uranium.
1789	Klaproth discovered zirconium.
1789-1799	French Revolution.
1792	Cotton gin (Eli Whitney).
1793	Benjamin Bell differentiated between gonorrhea and syphilis.
1793	Lowitz discovered mono- and trichloroacetic acids.
1793-1794	Reign of Terror in France.
1794	Lavoisier beheaded (May 8).
1794	Thomas Percival's code of medical ethics privately printed.
1795	Joseph B. Caventou, French pharmacist, scientist, born.
1795-1796	Société de Médecine de Paris founded.
1796	Jenner vaccinated James Phipps.
1796	Lowitz prepared absolute alcohol and pure ether.
1796-1815	Napoleonic Wars.
1797	Vauquelin discovered chromium.
1798	Jenner's *Inquiry* published.
1799	Davy discovered anesthetic properties of laughing gas (N_2O).
1800	"Royal College of Surgeons in London" chartered.
1801	Ritter experimented with ultraviolet rays.
1803	Fort Dearborn (present Chicago), Illinois, built.
1803	Klaproth discovered cerium.
1803-1808	Lewis and Clark explored the sources of the Mississippi.
1804-1815	Napoleon Emperor of the French.
1805	Battle of Trafalgar.
1805	Sertürner isolated morphine.
1806	End of Holy Roman Empire.
1806	Proust isolated mannitol.
1806	Vauquelin discovered cinchonic acid.
1809	McDowell performed ovariotomy.
1810	Figuier published qualities of animal charcoal.
1811	Massachusetts General Hospital (Boston) established.
1811	Courtois discovered iodine.
1811	Vauquelin discovered lecithin.

1813-1883	James Marion Sims.
1813-1879	Claude Bernard.
1815	Battle of Waterloo.
1815-1848	Horace Wells.
1815-1878	Crawford Long.
1816	Laennec invented stethoscope.
1817	Vauquelin discovered daphnin.
1817	Robiquet isolated narcotine.
1818	Caventou and Pelletier discovered strychnine.
1818	Meissner coined name "alkaloid."
1818-1865	Ignaz Philipp Semmelweis.
1819	Caventou and Pelletier discovered brucine and colchicine.
1819	Braconnet obtained grape sugar, treating sawdust with sulfuric acid.
1819-1868	William Thomas Green Morton.
1820	First *U. S. Pharmacopoeia* published.
1820	Caventou and Pelletier isolated quinine and cinchonine.
1821-1902	Rudolf Ludwig Carl Virchow.
1821	McGill College and University founded at Montreal.
1821	Runge isolated caffeine.
1821	Döbereiner discovered the process of catalysis.
1821-1894	Hermann L. F. von Helmholtz.
1821	Philadelphia College of Pharmacy founded.
1822	Serullas prepared iodoform.
1822	Louis Pasteur born.
1824	Braconnet discovered pectin, pectic acid.
1825	Jean-Martin Charcot born in Paris.
1825	*American Journal of Pharmacy*, first professional pharmacy periodical in English, published.
1826	Balard discovered bromine.
1827	Serullas discovered ethyl bromide.
1827	Wöhler isolated aluminum.
1827-1912	Lord Joseph Lister.
1829	Daguerre introduced photography.
1829	Tuéry demonstrated antidotal properties of charcoal.
1830	Kahler discovered santonin.
1830-1848	Reign of Louis Philippe.
1831	Guthrie, Liebig, and Soubeiran discovered chloroform.
1831	Soubeiran announced chloroform.
1831	Geiger prepared coniine.
1832	British Medical Association founded.
1832	Robiquet isolated codeine.
1832	Pelletier and Dumas isolated narceine.

GALEN—EXPERIMENTER IN DRUG COMPOUNDING

O F THE MEN of ancient times whose names are known and revered in both the professions of Pharmacy and Medicine, Galen undoubtedly is the foremost. Born in Pergamon in Asia Minor in 130 A.D., Galen practiced and taught both Pharmacy and Medicine in Rome. He died 70 years later in his native town; but his special brand of Hippocratian humoral pathology ruled Medicine in the Western world for 1500 years; and his name still is associated with that class of pharmaceuticals compounded by mechanical means which we call galenicals.

The importance of Galen to Pharmacy stems from the fact that in his books as well as in his practice and research he paid much attention to the correct compounding and use of drugs. He is credited with being "the father of polypharmacy;" and certainly some of his studies regarding the uses and actions of drugs might be classed as pharmacology. Galen was the originator of the formula for a cold cream, essentially similar to today's *Unguentum Aquae Rosae*—a formula about which fabulous cosmetic fortunes have been built.

Galen also is supposed to have stated that "the people want drugs," and to have acted accordingly in his own practice. Other fortunes have been built upon modern interpretations of this Galenism.

Not only did Galen have, in his Roman period, an "iatreion," the usual room in which Greco-Roman physicians received their patients and dispensed their remedies; he also had an "apotheca," or store and preparation room. That he was a showman, as well as pharmacist, physician, and scientific experimenter, there seems little doubt. Beginning his career as physician to the gladiators, Galen became physician to Roman emperors and to the cream of

GALEN—EXPERIMENTER IN DRUG COMPOUNDING

Of the men of ancient times whose names are known and revered in both the professions of Pharmacy and Medicine, Galen, undoubtedly, is the foremost. Galen (130-200 A.D.) practiced and taught both Pharmacy and Medicine in Rome; his principles of preparing and compounding medicines ruled in the Western world for 1,500 years; and his name still is associated with that class of pharmaceuticals compounded by mechanical means—galenicals. He was the originator of the formula for a cold cream, essentially similar to that known today. Many procedures Galen originated have their counterparts in today's modern compounding laboratories.

Roman society of his time, the wealthy and the aristocrats. Galen prepared his medicaments himself, and his treatises dealing with the preparation and use of drugs contain a profusion of formulas. Among his many and varied publications are no less than thirty books touching on Pharmacy. His formulas indicate a most intelligent use of opium, hyoscyamus, hellebore, colocynth, grape juice, wine, and cold compresses.

Paul Diepgen in his *History of Medicine* describes Galen's ideas on the efficacy of drugs as follows: "The concept 'remedy' is sharply defined. Everything that effects a change in the organism is a 'remedy' (drug) in contrast to foodstuffs which are substance-increasing. Like everything in the world, the drugs likewise consist of the elements, (as at that time conceived) fire, water, earth, and air, hence have the 'primary' quality of the latter, being hot and moist, dry and cold. It is these qualities that determine the effect. It is not the obvious characteristics such as color, smell and taste, from which conclusions may be made as to the effect of drugs, but experience and experiment with regard to the particular way in which the organism reacts to the application of the drug. There are three different groups of medicaments: the action of the first group is determined by 'primary' qualities; the effect of a second group is due to 'secondary' qualities, i.e., to the way in which the drugs concerned affect our senses; the third group of drugs acts through 'tertiary' qualities (their whole substance, i.e., their effect cannot be explained by their being hot and moist, cold and dry) and produce an effect analogous to that which we call 'specific' today . . ." Galen attempted to find a scientific basis for the dispensing of drugs, and to introduce cautious, individualized dosage—a procedure which undoubtedly was of advantage to his patients.

To further his knowledge of the action of drugs, and to assure more dependable and accurate results from his treatments, Galen developed many methods for mixing, extracting, refining and combining drugs. These ideas carried over into the late eighteenth century, and have their counterparts today in compounding, both at the prescription counter in the retail pharmacy and in the large manufacturing laboratory.

"Learned experimenter, endowed with a keen philosophical mind"—that was Galen, according to Meunier—"outstanding and considerate diagnostician, and fortunate eclectic therapeutist, the skillful showman who was extremely successful in attracting attention and drawing limelight upon himself." There are curtain calls for Galen in the field of Pharmacy even after these 1800 years of trial, error, and scientific development.

WORLD EVENTS AND PHARMACY HISTORY

Dates, persons, and events of significance to the evolution of Pharmacy include:

1833	Pelletier and Dumas discovered thebaine.
1833	Braconnet discovered dextrin.
1833	Johannes Müller's treatise on physiology published.
1833	William Beaumont published experiments on gastric digestion.
1834	Runge isolated carbolic acid.
1834	Runge discovered aniline.
1834	Dumas obtained and named pure chloroform.
1835	Berzelius coined the term "catalysis."
1837	Gerhard differentiated between typhus and typhoid fevers.
1837	Victoria became Queen of England.
1839	Schwann published treatise on the cell theory.
1840	Henle published statement of germ theory of communicable diseases.
1841	Pharmaceutical Society of Great Britain founded.
1843	O. W. Holmes pointed out contagiousness of puerperal fever.
1844	Rose discovered niobium (Columbium).
1845	Wilhelm Conrad Röntgen born.
1846	Morton introduced ether anesthesia (October 16).
1846	J. Marion Sims devised a vaginal speculum.
1847	American Medical Association organized.
1847	Helmholtz published treatise on *Conservation of Energy*.
1847	Virchow founded *Archiv für Pathologische Anatomie und Physiologie und für Klinische Medizin* (Berlin).
1847	Sir J. Y. Simpson introduced chloroform anesthesia.
1847	Semmelweis discovered pathogenesis of puerperal fever.
1848	Fehling introduced test for sugar in urine.
1848	Claude Bernard demonstrated that glycogen is synthesized in the liver.
1849	J. Marion Sims successfully operated for vesico-vaginal fistula.
1850	Claude Bernard published studies on arrow poisons.
1850	Fehling developed solution for detection of sugar.

DAMIAN AND COSMAS
PHARMACY'S PATRON SAINTS

Twinship of the health professions, Pharmacy and Medicine, is nowhere more strikingly portrayed than in the record of life's work, art, history and legend that has come down to us concerning Damian and Cosmas.

Twin brothers of Arabian descent, and devout Christians, Damian and Cosmas practiced the twin professions in the second half of the third century A.D., offering the solace of religion as well as the benefit of their medical and pharmaceutical knowledge to the sick who pilgrimaged to their home in Egea (Cilicia), in Asia Minor.

Having inherited considerable wealth, the twin brothers are reputed to have offered their services and drugs gratuitously to the steadily growing numbers of sufferers who came to them from all parts of Asia Minor and adjacent areas. Many reports of seeming miraculous cures which they achieved have been recorded.

The beneficial work of Damian and Cosmas came to a sudden end when, on February 24, 303 A.D., the Roman Emperor, Diocletian, issued his edict for persecution of those of the Christian faith, leaving all Christians only the choice: abjuration of their faith, or death. In the province of Cilicia, the Roman Prefect, Lysias, a sworn enemy of the new religion, was especially eager to follow the edict to the letter; and the twins, Damian and Cosmas, were among the first to be arrested. Wootton describes the legend of their fate as follows:

"Being condemned to be drowned, it is related that an angel severed their bonds so that they could gain the shore. They were then ordered to be burnt; but the fire attacked their executioners, several of whom were killed. Next, they were fastened to a cross and archers shot arrows at them. The arrows, however, were turned from them and struck those who had placed them on the crosses. Finally they were beheaded, and their souls were seen

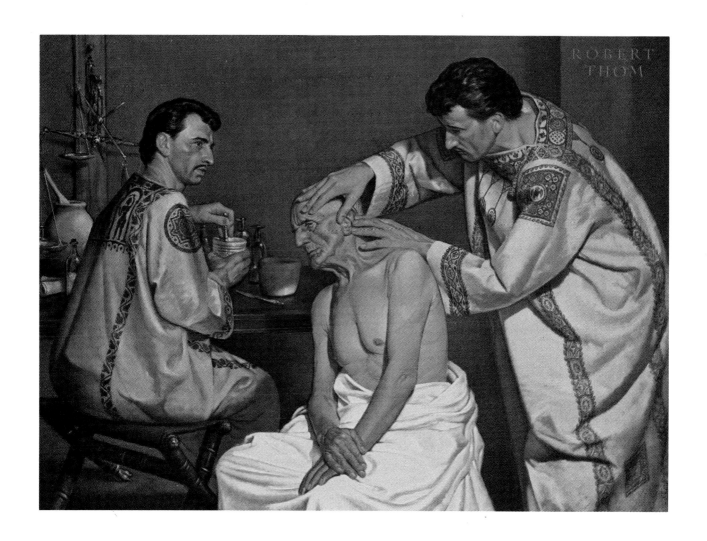

DAMIAN AND COSMAS—PHARMACY'S PATRON SAINTS

Twinship of the health professions, Pharmacy and Medicine, is nowhere more strikingly portrayed than by Damian, the apothecary, and Cosmas, the physician. Twin brothers of Arabian descent, and devout Christians, they offered the solace of religion as well as the benefit of their knowledge to the sick who visited them. Their twin careers were cut short in the year 303 by martyrdom. For centuries their tomb in the Syrian city of Cyprus was a shrine. Churches were built in their honor in Rome and other cities. After canonization, they became the patron saints of Pharmacy and Medicine, and many miracles were attributed to them.

mounting heavenward. For centuries their tomb at Cyrus, in Syria, was a shrine where miracles of healing were performed, and in the sixth century the Emperor Justinian, who believed he had been cured of a serious illness by their intercession, not only beautified and fortified the Syrian city, but also built a beautiful church in their honor at Constantinople (Byzantium). Later, their relics were removed to Rome, and Pope Felix consecrated a church to them there. Physicians and pharmacists throughout Catholic Europe celebrated their memory on September 27 for centuries." This date still is observed by medical and pharmaceutical organizations in several countries.

Urdang observes that "it is significant of the high esteem in which the two saints were held in early Christianity that the church devoted to Cosmas and Damian by Pope Felix IV (526-530) was the first one to be erected on the Roman forum." In a summary of his recent research devoted to Cosmas and Damian, Professor Walter Artelt of the University of Frankfurt A.M. (Germany) says the following:

"Sick people now were gathering in the Cosmas and Damian sanctuaries—as they did in earlier days in the sanctuaries devoted to the cult of Asclepios—and were given their medical treatment, and, in falling asleep, waited for the appearance of the two saints. The famous Cosmas and Damian Church, established in a suburb of Constantinople in the fifth century, was supplemented by a hospital and a pharmacy."

The story of Damian and Cosmas has captured the interest of many artists and sculptors throughout the centuries. Damian usually is represented in the role of the apothecary, with significant instruments in his profession; while Cosmas usually is shown with a urine glass, the symbol of the physician, since in ancient times physical examination of the urine was considered one of the foremost means of diagnosis. Among the masters who recorded the miracles and scenes from the lives of Cosmas and Damian were Botticelli, Fra Filippo Lippi, Michelangelo, Tintoretto, Titian, and Fra Angelico.

Artists usually have represented the twin healers, martyrs, and saints in the costume and physiognomy of the artist's time and locale, and with saintly halos about their heads; only Höfer, a German painter, in 1932 depicted the saints as Arabs, showing the characteristic features of the race, dressed in Arabic fashion, and placed in Arabic surroundings. Robert Thom has visualized them as men of flesh and blood, at the peak of their twin careers of service, in the surroundings and costumes of their day, and before canonization, which, of course, occurred several centuries after their martyrdom.

Separated as to their special roles, and yet united in their beneficial work, these twin patron saints of Pharmacy and Medicine symbolize perfectly the early recognition of the necessary unity as well as the division of labor and responsibility between the twin professions which form the foundation of the healing arts.

MONASTIC PHARMACY

DURING the Middle Ages (sometimes referred to as the Dark Ages) much of the Western world's cultural and scientific knowledge of earlier civilizations was destroyed by the various conquests and reprisals between Romans and Christians, and later, the conquering invaders from the north. The remnants of antique knowledge of Pharmacy and Medicine were preserved and utilized principally in the monasteries. The monks did much to keep the torch of the sciences alight during this period. As the care of the sick became accepted as a duty of the Christian church, the old pagan deities of the healing arts were replaced by saints, such as the twin pharmacist-physician martyrs, Damian and Cosmas.

The first attempt at systematizing this Christian endeavor was made by Marcus Aurelius Cassiodorus (490-585), Chancellor to the Ostrogothic King Theodoric and his successors at Ravenna. Greek books were translated into Latin by the monks, and the Latin writings on Pharmacy and Medicine were preserved in monastery libraries. The brethren of some of the orders included many of the greatest scholars of the time.

Finally, Gerbert of Aurillac, (who later became Pope Sylvester II) after having visited Spain about 967, brought the scientific studies in the monasteries to new blossom and was the first transmitter of Arabian wisdom to northern Europe.

Pharmacy and medicine are known to have been practiced and taught as early as in the seventh, eighth and ninth centuries in cloisters in England and Ireland, in France, in Switzerland, and in Germany. Under Charlemagne, schools were established in the monasteries; and among the subjects taught, medico-pharmaceutical science and technique had their part.

It was the function of the monk-apothecary to prepare medicines and administer them to the sick under the supervision of the monk-physician. Together, they had charge of the hospital and infirmary

MONASTIC PHARMACY

During the Middle Ages remnants of the Western knowledge of Pharmacy and Medicine were preserved in the monasteries (fifth to twelfth centuries). These sciences are known to have been taught in the cloisters as early as the seventh century. Manuscripts from many lands were translated or copied for monastery libraries. The monks gathered herbs and simples in the field, or raised them in their own herb gardens. These they prepared according to the art of the apothecary for the benefit of the sick and injured. Gardens such as these still may be found in monasteries in many countries.

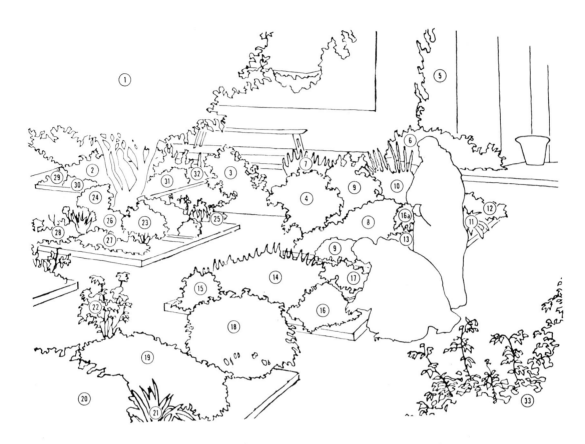

Key to plants in the picture, *Monastic Pharmacy*

The herbs, flowers, shrubs, and trees appearing in the picture, *Monastic Pharmacy*, were identified by Esther Ann Huebner, gardener at The Cloisters, Fort Tyron Park, New York City, which is operated as a branch of The Metropolitan Museum of Art. These plants were regarded as having pharmaceutical and medical significance during medieval times.

1. *Mespilus germanica*—Medlar Tree
2. *Salvia officinalis*—Sage
3. *Rosa centifolia*—Cabbage Rose
4. *Rosa gallica* var. *versicolor*—Rosa Mundi
5. Espallier Pear Tree
6. *Capsicum annuum*—Red Peppers
7. *Artemisia abrotanum*—Southernwood
8. *Melissa officinalis*—Lemon Balm
9. *Agrimonia eupatoria*—Agrimony
10. *Cichorium intybus*—Chicory
11. *Cheiranthus cheiri*—Wallflower
12. *Sedum telephium*—Orpine
13. *Dianthus plumarius*—Grass Pink
14. *Rosmarinus officinalis*—Rosemary
15, 16, } *Satureja montana*—Winter
16a, 17. }   Savory

18. *Ruta graveolen*—Rue
19. *Mentha spicata*—Spearmint
20. *Datura stramonium*—Stramonium
21. *Urginea scilla*—Sea Onion, Squill
22. *Rosa damascena* var. *versicolor*—York and Lancaster Rose
23, 24, 25. *Rosa damascena*—Damask Rose
26. *Hesperis matronalis*—Dame's Rocket
27. *Aquilegia vulgaris*—Columbine
28. *Campanula rotundifolia*—Bluebell of Scotland
29, 32. *Artemesia dracunculus*—Tarragon
30. *Thymus serpyllum* var. *vulgaris*—Lemon Thyme
31. *Petroselinum crispum*—Curled Parsley
33. *Rosa gallica*—French Rose

of the monastery and gave aid to the sick and injured who came to their doors.

The materia medica of the monastic apothecary was mainly drawn from the vegetable kingdom, and, at first, the neighboring woods and fields furnished most of the herbs and simple remedies. Later, the monks began to cultivate in their own herb gardens plants which had been proved by experience to be most effective.

To ancient monk-apothecaries, who linked healing of the soul with healing of the body, who preserved the records of the past and carried forward the light of learning and investigation, Pharmacy indeed owes much.

WORLD EVENTS AND PHARMACY HISTORY

Dates, persons, and events of significance to the evolution of Pharmacy include:

1851	Helmholtz invented ophthalmoscope.		1860	Pasteur demonstrated presence of bacteria in air.
1851	Walter Reed born.		1860	Niemann isolated pure cocaine.
1851-53	Pravaz introduced hypodermic syringe.		1861	Victor Emmanuel became first King of Italy.
1852	American Pharmaceutical Association founded.		1861-65	Civil War in the United States.
1852	Santiago Ramón y Cajal born.		1862	Florence Nightingale established training school for nurses at St. Thomas's Hospital.
1852-70	Second Empire in France; Napoleon III became Emperor.		1862	Dr. Samuel P. Duffield began a small pharmaceutical manufacturing business in Detroit, Michigan.
1854-56	Crimean War: Florence Nightingale.		
1854	Paul Ehrlich born.		1863	Old Cook County Hospital (Chicago) started.
1855	J. Marion Sims founded hospital for women's diseases (New York City).		1863	American Veterinary Medical Association (Detroit) founded.
			1863	National Academy of Sciences (Washington) founded.
1855	Gaedcke announced cocaine from coca leaves.		1864	Traube studied pathology of fever.
1856	Sir W. H. Perkin (1838-1907) obtained aniline dyes (coal-tar products).		1864	Gray Herbarium (Harvard University) founded.
1858	Virchow's *Cellularpathologie* published.		1864	Chicago Medical College incorporated.
1859	Darwin's *Origin of Species* published.		1864	St. Louis College of Pharmacy founded.

THE FIRST APOTHECARY SHOPS

As FAR AS we know, it was in Bagdad in the last quarter of the eighth century that there were established privately owned stores for preparing and dealing in drugs. For the first time in recorded history, the profession of Pharmacy had a definite place of its own as a part of a public health system. It was not until the next century, however, that there is evidence of existence of educated pharmacists, and of governmental inspection and regulation of pharmacists and sellers of drugs and herbs.

There had been, in Greece and Rome, a number of retailers in drugs who in many cases acted as compounders; but they were regarded as intruding upon the rights and even the duties of the physicians rather than as performing a real and legitimate service. The division of labor and responsibility between the physician as the prescriber, and the pharmacist as the legitimate compounder and dispenser of the prescription, had not become a recognized concept, and still less an accepted reality, in the Greco-Roman period.

Significance of Arabian contributions to the science of Pharmacy may be grasped by comparison with the rest of the world from the fifth to the twelfth centuries. While there had developed in ancient Egypt, and still more in the Western world of antiquity, a considerable knowledge of drugs and their therapeutic uses, the modes of preparation still remained rather primitive and limited. Destruction of many libraries and schools, which had begun in the conflicts between the Romans and the Christians, and was later carried on by invading Vandals, Longobardi, Visigoths and Ostrogoths, had reduced Western knowledge of the sciences largely to that remnant preserved and kept alive in the seclusion of the monasteries. During this period of Western decay, the Arabic-Mohammedan world not only became heir to Greco-Roman wisdom, but, at least as far as the knowledge of nature and its treasures and their medicinal application was concerned, added to it. Arabia was the habitat of

THE FIRST APOTHECARY SHOPS

The Arabs separated the arts of apothecary and physician, establishing in Bagdad late in the eighth century the first privately owned drug stores. They preserved much of the Greco-Roman wisdom, added to it, developing with the aid of their natural resources syrups, confections, conserves, distilled waters and alcoholic liquids. The apothecary is examining logs of sandalwood offered by a traveling merchant, while children indulge their taste for sweets with stalks of sugar cane. When the Moslems swept across Africa, Spain and southern France, they carried with them a new pattern of Pharmacy which western Europe soon assimilated.

53

the trees and shrubs that supplied the then known world with aromatic gums and valuable spices. Persian, Indian and Chinese drugs unknown to the Greco-Roman world, such as camphor, cassia, cloves, cubeb, musk, nutmeg, rhubarb, sandalwood, senna, and tamarind, were described in the treatises of authors writing in Arabic; and in crude form or in preparations compounded therefrom, filled the shelves and drawers of the newly established apothecary shops.

Sugar cane grew in the areas occupied by the Arabs, hence sugar could be and was produced at a reasonable price. This gave rise to a number of new types of pharmaceutical preparations requiring the skill of the experts: among them, syrups of all kinds, confections, and conserves. The distillation of aromatic waters, and somewhat later, of alcoholic preparations, became almost a monopoly of the Arabian pharmacists.

The Arabs also cultivated the study of chemistry (alchemy), which they brought to bear on their knowledge of plants and herbs. Our knowledge of such chemicals as sodium carbonate, potassium nitrate, corrosive sublimate, and lead acetate stems from the Arabs.

Several passages by the Arabian authors prove that there were opportunities for securing pharmaceutical education during and after the first third of the ninth century.

Among the Arabs, the practice of the apothecary's art became more and more distinct from that of the physician. The Arabian apothecaries were also known as "Sayādilah," which some authors interpret as a reference to their dealing in sandalwood, then thought to have many therapeutic uses.

"The apothecary shop," says Tschirch, "is a specific Arabian creation . . . and it is very doubtful whether Pharmacy would have developed in the way in which it did, if European medicine had remained free from Arabian influence."

An early apothecary shop in Bagdad, according to Thompson, was kept by Abu Coreisch Isa el-Seidelani. Bagdad, at that time, was a large and populous city of nearly a million inhabitants. Arabian apothecary shops were open fronted like many of their European sister institutions up to the fifteenth century.

A nomad race, the Arabs at the height of their ascendancy spread westwards from the Persian Gulf, along the northern coast of Africa, across the Mediterranean into Sicily, Spain and Southern France, carrying with them their arts and customs. To a large degree they set the pattern which the profession of Pharmacy was to follow in the Western world.

WORLD EVENTS AND PHARMACY HISTORY

Dates, persons, and events of significance to the evolution of Pharmacy include:

1865	Joseph Lister introduced antiseptic treatment of wounds.
1865	Gregor Mendel published memoir on plant hybridity.
1865	Claude Bernard published "An Introduction to the Study of Experimental Medicine."
1865	Cornell University founded.
1865	Pasteur studied silkworm diseases.
1865	Ignaz Semmelweis died.
1865	Billings founded U. S. Army Medical Library.
1865	First International Pharmaceutical Congress convened, Brunswick, Germany.
1865-1866	Villemin demonstrated transmissibility of tuberculosis by inoculation (Klencke, 1843).
1866	J. Marion Sims published "Clinical Notes on Uterine Surgery."
1866	A. J. Ångström introduced Ångström units.
1866	Metropolitan Health Board (New York City) established.
1866	Duffield, Parke & Company formed as partnership in Detroit, Michigan. (Beginning of Parke, Davis & Company.)

1867	Lister introduced antiseptic surgery.
1867	Helmholtz published treatise on physiological optics.
1867	Bobbs performed cholecystotomy.
1867	A. W. von Hoffmann discovered formaldehyde.
1867	First International Medical Congress at Paris.
1867	Dominion of Canada established.
1867	Opening of Suez Canal and of Pacific Railway.
1867	Canadian Medical Association organized.
1867	Chicago Board of Health organized.
1868	University of Tokyo (Tokyo Tcikoku Daigaku) founded.
1868	Allbutt introduced clinical thermometer.
1868	Darwin published treatise on *The Variation of Animals and Plants Under Domestication*.
1868	Hering and Breurer discovered self-regulation of respiration (rôle of vagus).
1868	Society of Czechoslovakian Physicians (Prague).
1868	Société de Médecine Légale (Paris) founded.

55

AVICENNA
THE "PERSIAN GALEN"

THERE IS in almost every field of endeavor one genius through whom the essential achievements of his period are expressed in such perfection that he seems to stand for his time. In relation to Arabian Pharmacy and Medicine, that man was the Persian, Pur-i-sina, known in Arabic as Ibn Sina, and called Avicenna by the Western world.

According to George Sarton, Avicenna was "the most famous scientist of Islam and one of the most famous of all races, places and times." More recently, in connection with the celebration in 1952 of Avicenna's millennium under the auspices of the Iranian government, Ali Asghar Hekmat referred to Avicenna as "the absolute Prince over realms of philosophy and medicine from the eleventh up to the eighteenth century . . . the loyal agent for the transportation of ideas between the Orient and the Occident all through the long period of the Middle Ages as well as in the Renaissance."

There were great scientists writing in Arabic both before and after Avicenna. The work of al-Razi, called Rhazes, who died about 923, equalled that of his later compatriot in scientific importance and meaning to Pharmacy. The book of simple drugs, authored about 200 years after Avicenna by the Spanish-born Ibn-al-Baitar (1197-1248), offered to Pharmacy the greatest number of drugs (more than 2000) ever presented in a very methodical and critical compilation. And yet, whenever Arabian Pharmacy or Medicine is mentioned, it is Avicenna whose name appears first and predominantly.

It was about 980 that a boy named "Hussein," grandson of the Persian, Sina, a well-to-do state functionary, was born in the city

AVICENNA—THE "PERSIAN GALEN"

Among the brilliant contributors to the sciences of Pharmacy and Medicine during the Arabian era was one genius who seems to stand for his time—the Persian, Ibn Sina (about 980-1037 A.D.), called Avicenna by the Western world. Pharmacist, physician, poet, philosopher and diplomat, Avicenna was an intellectual giant, a companion of Persian princes and rulers. He wrote in Arabic, often while secluded in the home of an apothecary friend. His pharmaceutical teachings were accepted as authoritative in the West until the 17th century; still are dominant influences in the Orient.

of Bukhara, in Central Asia. He became better known in the West as Avicenna. At an early age, he exhibited a powerful mind. He wrote most of his works in Arabic, which in the Orient was analogous to Latin in the Western world. At the age of 17, he was so celebrated in Medicine that he was called upon to attend Nuh, son of Mansur, the Samanid Ruler of Bukhara, and cure him of a dangerous disease. As a reward, he asked the king to allow him access to the Royal Library.

The enormous breadth of Avicenna's intellectual endeavors—philosophy, poetry, and diplomacy as well as pharmacy, medicine and natural science—made him outstanding in his period. During his 58 years, he traveled extensively, studying the great works of the age, teaching a multitude of pupils, writing about 200 books and treatises, and administering for the state as a Vizir. From time to time, he was the companion and favorite of the ruling Princes, who encouraged his scientific works. He was not always successful as a diplomat, however, and spent some part of his later life in prison or in hiding. But even in those hard moments, he did not waste his time; many treatises were compiled in concealment.

It was Avicenna's main medical work, his *Canon Medicinae*, which can be regarded as "the final codification of all Greco-Arabic medicine." Its impression on the medical and pharmaceutical world in the Orient and Occident was enormous. The *Canon* was an authority taught and referred to up to the seventeenth century. In the Orient it is still dominant.

Of the five books into which the *Canon* is divided, the second deals with the simple drugs and the fifth with compounded remedies. Adopting and elaborating on Galen's ideas, Avicenna earned the cognomen of "The Arabian Galen."

A large part of this *Canon*, so important to Pharmacy, was written by Avicenna after his escape from political imprisonment and while he lived concealed in the home of an apothecary friend. In this, he paid much attention to the right ways of preparing drugs. He recommended gilding and silvering of pills, not only as a means of covering bad smell or taste of the ingredients, but because of his belief in the blood-purifying effects of these noble metals. He used iron in various forms, and advised that food and drink be acidulated with a little sour milk or vinegar.

Avicenna exerted such an enormous mental energy that his physical body could not endure for long. His life ended in 1037 in Hamadan (the ancient Ecbatana), and his tomb still exists. Under the patronage of the Iranian government, a monument was built over the tomb in 1952, and a commemorative postal stamp issued pertaining to Avicenna, the scientist, who, though born a Persian, belongs to the world.

WORLD EVENTS AND PHARMACY HISTORY

Dates, persons, and events of significance to the evolution of Pharmacy include:

1869	University of Warsaw founded.
1869	Brown-Séquard introduced doctrine of internal secretions.
1869	Virchow urged medical inspection of schools.
1869	Harvey Williams Cushing born.
1869	Oscar Liebreich demonstrated hypnotic effect of chloral hydrate.
1869	Ceylon Medical College founded.
1869	American Museum of Natural History (New York City) founded.
1869	Chicago Medical College became Medical Department of Northwestern University.
1869	Massachusetts State Board of Health created.
1869	Ontario (Canada) Act for Registration of Vital Statistics.
1870	Fritsch and Hitzig investigated localization of functions of brain.
1870	Linoleum invented.
1870	Wisconsin Academy of Sciences founded.
1870	Anthropological Society of Vienna founded.
1870-71	Franco-Prussian War (test of vaccination).

1871	Establishment of German Empire and French Republic.
1871	Darwin's *Descent of Man and Selection in Relation to Sex* published.
1871	Hammarsten discovered rôle of fibrinogen in coagulation of blood.
1871	Royal Anthropological Institute (London) founded.
1871	Walter Bradford Cannon born.
1871	Joseph Lister noted antibiotic phenomena.
1871-72	First American filter for water supply at Poughkeepsie, New York.
1872	Carlos Finlay (Cuba) declared that mosquitoes transmitted yellow fever.
1872	University of Adelaide (Australia) founded.
1872	Abbé introduced oil immersion lenses.
1872	Merck introduced pyoctanin (methyl violet).
1872	American Public Health Association held first meeting (September 12).
1873	Obermeier discovered spirillum of relapsing fever.

SEPARATION OF PHARMACY
AND MEDICINE

PHARMACY'S POSITION in history has been impelled toward its great and rich heritage by the acts of many strong personalities. In not a few instances, such actions were inaugurated by persons in other walks of life. The measures which they initiated arose from a keen personal understanding of the uniqueness and value of Pharmacy's service to humanity. There is no question, however, that this insight grew from, and was supported by, the quiet, persistent work of now-nameless pharmacists who loved their profession and contributed to it qualities that lifted it above the commonplace.

Among world leaders who advanced Pharmacy's cause, none had a more colorful or fascinating personality than Frederick II of Hohenstaufen, Emperor of Germany and King of the Two Sicilies —the living link between the Oriental and Occidental worlds of the thirteenth century. It was he who first gave Pharmacy its legal independence as a profession.

The seventh to the twelfth centuries saw Islam and Christianity as well as Judaism in intimate contact in Spain and the Sicilies. Sicily and Spain were the two principal points from which the Latin West drew on Greco-Arabic medicine. After the fall of the Sicilian city of Syracuse into the hands of the Arabs in 878, Sicily became a seat of Arabic culture until the year 1061, when the Normans began the conquest of the island, completing it in 1091. (In the days of the Hohenstaufen emperors, Sicily was a twin kingdom, including not only the island, but the toe, heel, and part of the calf of the Italian "boot.")

Here and there in the European countries exposed to Arabian cultural influence, public pharmacies began to appear in the

SEPARATION OF PHARMACY AND MEDICINE

In European countries exposed to Arabian influence, public pharmacies began to appear in the 11th century. However, it was not until about 1240 A.D. that, in Sicily and southern Italy, Pharmacy was legally separated from Medicine. Frederick II of Hohenstaufen, Emperor of Germany as well as King of Sicily, was a living link between Oriental and Occidental worlds. At his palace in Palermo, he presented his subject Pharmacists with the first European edict completely separating their responsibilities from those of Medicine, and prescribing regulations for their professional practice.

61

eleven century, and perhaps even earlier. But it was not until about 1240, as Frederick II concluded the legislative reorganization of the war-torn and politically torn kingdom of the Two Sicilies, which he inherited from his mother, that Pharmacy was legally separated from Medicine and made an integral part of a public welfare system following Arabian patterns.

Though half Norman by blood, one-quarter French and one-quarter Italian, Frederick II was definitely Italianate in his ways. Brought up in intimate contact with Moslems and Jews as well as Christians, he not only was polylingual but introduced into his reign the best and most effective ideas from each of the cultures whose paths crossed in Palermo, his headquarters. An orphan at 13, King at 17, his dominant personality tempered on the anvil of almost insurmountable obstacles, he nevertheless reorganized his holdings and became a most brilliant ruler, one of the most learned men of his day and a legislator of the first order. Frederick II revived the medical school at Salerno and founded the University of Naples, opening the doors to scientists of every faith, Moslems, Jews and Christians. His court at Palermo was a meeting place of the flower of knighthood and of science, filled with scientists, soldiers, diplomats, dignitaries and representatives of all faiths. It was there that, during a historic moment, in 1240, Frederick II, having heard the case for and against the apothecaries, by imperial edict granted his subject pharmacists their professional independence.

Frederick's grant was not without its safeguards, however. In his wisdom, he surrounded the privilege with responsibilities, several of which parallel closely requirements in our codes today.

The most essential regulations concerning Pharmacy in the law of Frederick II were:

1. Complete separation of the pharmaceutical profession from the medical profession, forbidding any business relation between physician and pharmacist, either in open or hidden partnership.

2. Official supervision of pharmaceutical practice, with rigid penalties in cases of violations of the duties of a pharmacist toward his customers.

3. Compulsory use of a prescribed formulary, a kind of pharmacopoeia, in order to guarantee the reliability and uniformity of the drugs of the apothecary.

Two further rules provided for a limitation of the number of the pharmacies to be licensed, and for governmentally fixed prices for drugs. While the first three rules have achieved well-nigh universal application in the centuries that followed, the latter two were put into practice in most of the countries coming into the sphere of German politico-cultural influence and in part in Latin Europe. They were not put into practice in the Anglo-Saxon world.

It is particularly significant that, while violations of the duties of pharmacists were punished "by the confiscation of their movable goods," (property loss only) Frederick's laws imposed upon the official inspectors who "should allow any fraud" the punishment of death.

THE FIRST OFFICIAL
PHARMACOPOEIA

ONE OF THE earliest impressions received by the student in Pharmacy is to think of the pharmacopoeia as "The Pharmacist's Bible"—the book of standards to which he is enjoined to conform in preparing and dispensing medicines intended to be prescribed by physicians. Not only is the comparison to the Christian volume of divine edict an apt simile; the word, bible, derived from the Latin, denotes "book"—a book looked upon as authoritative. One of the chief objects of such official publications has been to ensure uniformity of composition of preparations and purity of substances to be used as medicines.

It was in Florence that the idea originated for development of a pharmacopoeia with official status, to be followed by all apothecaries within the jurisdiction of the city-state's political authority. This goal was realized for the first time on European soil in 1498, with the publication of the *Nuovo Receptario*.

Medieval Italy owed its economic blossoming mainly to the circumstance that the wares of the Orient had to pass through Italian hands before they reached other European countries. From the twelfth to the sixteenth centuries, Italian trade extended from Constantinople, Damascus, Alexandria and Tunis to South Germany, France, England, the Iberian peninsula, and Holland. It was particularly Florence, Genoa and Venice which dominated the European trade in oriental drugs and spices. It was in 1498, too, that Vasco de Gama found an all-water route to the East Indies and brought the treasures of the Far East to eager hands. (Columbus had discovered a strange new continent in the western seas only six years earlier.)

It was not so much the lack of books listing simple drugs and formulas for the preparation of compounded ones, that brought about the first pharmacopoeia. Rather, it was the different views

64

THE FIRST OFFICIAL PHARMACOPOEIA

The idea of a pharmacopoeia with official status, to be followed by all apothecaries, originated in Florence. The Nuovo Receptario, *originally written in Italian, was published and became the legal standard for the city-state in 1498. It was the result of collaboration of the Guild of Apothecaries and the Medical Society—one of the earliest manifestations of constructive interprofessional relations. The professional groups received official advice and guidance from the powerful Dominican monk, Savonarola, (seated, foreground) who, at the time, was the political leader in Florence.*

65

expressed and the varying interpretation given in private literature. This confusion gave rise to demands for some standard that would warrant uniformity in kind and strength of drugs prescribed by physicians and dispensed by pharmacists.

The title of this first official European pharmacopoeia was conspicuous in its simplicity—*Nuovo Receptario Composto dal Famossisimo Chollegio Degli Eximii Doctori della Arte et Medicina della Inclita Cipta di Firenze.* In English translation: "New Formulary Compiled by the Most Renowned College of the Distinguished Doctors of the Arts and Medicine of the Magnificent City of Florence." There was reason for this simplicity of title and lack of any of the prefaces or phrases dedicated to people in authority which were so common in those times of autocratic government. At the date of publication of the book (January 10, 1498) there was nobody in the city of Florence to whom such a dedication could properly (and safely!) be directed. The Medici family, whose members had lorded over the republic for about a century, had been driven out and were living in exile, while the power of the monk and religious reformer, Girolamo Savonarola, who had grown into the actual leadership of Florence since 1494, was rapidly fading. As a matter of fact, it was in this same year (1498) that Savonarola was condemned to death and perished at the stake.

Noteworthy is the fact that in the preface of the volume, it is stated that the book was compiled by physicians "at the request of the executive officers of the guild of apothecaries," and it carries the seal of the apothecaries' guild as a sign of its official status. It was printed in Florence (printing had been developed only shortly before) and is a small folio volume measuring about 9 x 10½ inches. It has no pagination and consists of eighty-eight leaves.

Many meetings must have taken place in Florence in late 1497, wherein representatives of the apothecaries' guild and of the college of medicine met to work on the text of the book, with advice and guidance from the powerful Dominican monk, Savonarola, then in authority. The Italian apothecaries were always considered patricians, and played an important role in the political and social life of their country. The endeavor from which the *Nuovo Receptario* was produced is perhaps one of the earliest manifestations of that progressive, cooperative spirit that has come to be known as interprofessional relations.

The content of the *Nuovo Receptario* was based entirely on the Greco-Arabic drug therapy of the time. Its purpose was not to promote or even represent progress, but to provide for uniformity and to furnish the pharmacists with a handy book for daily use. This first official European pharmaceutical standard was not written in the language of the learned, Latin, but in the vernacular, Italian. It was, however, translated into Latin in 1518 and was thus made available to those interested all over the Western world.

Some fifty years were to elapse before the example of Florence was followed and official pharmacopoeias began to appear in other political jurisdictions.

WORLD EVENTS AND PHARMACY HISTORY

Dates, persons, and events of significance to the evolution of Pharmacy include:

1874	Cholera conference in Vienna.
1874	Joseph Goldberger born.
1874	Fiedler stressed danger of morphine habit.
1874	Willy Kühne discovered trypsin.
1875	Faculté de Médecine et Pharmacie (Lille) founded.
1875	Landois discovered hemolysis from transfusion of alien blood.
1875	Hardy and Gerard introduced pilocarpine.
1875	Chesebrough obtained vaseline.
1875	English Public Health Act.
1875	Boston Medical Library founded (opened October 18).
1876	Imperial Board of Health founded at Berlin (April 30).
1876	Royal Sanitary Institute founded (London).
1876	Johns Hopkins University founded.
1876	Royal Academy of Medicine founded at Rome.
1876	Kolbe isolated salicylic acid.
1876	Koch obtained pure cultures of anthrax bacilli on artificial media.
1876	Pictet invented artificial manufacture of ice.
1876	Max Nitze introduced cystoscope.
1876	American Dermatological Association (Boston) founded.
1876	Bell telephone introduced.
1876	American Chemical Society (Washington, D. C.) founded.
1876-1909	New Cook County Hospital (Chicago) begun and completed.
1877	Pasteur discovered bacillus of malignant edema.
1877	L. Pasteur and J. Joubert observed antibiotic phenomena.
1877	Esmarch introduced aseptic bandage.
1877	Ernst von Bergmann introduced corrosive sublimate antisepsis.
1877-1878	Bollinger and Israel described actinomycosis.
1878	Koch discovered causes of traumatic infections.
1878	J. Marion Sims performed cholecystotomy.
1878	Von Basch measured blood pressure with sphygmomanometer.
1878	Claude Bernard died.

THE SOCIETY OF
APOTHECARIES OF LONDON

TRADE in drugs and spices was a lucrative pursuit in the Middle Ages. In the British Isles, this trade was largely a monopoly in the hands of the Guild of Pepperers in London. First record of this group appeared in 1180. The name was changed to the Company of Grocers in 1428, when it received a charter as a special grant from Henry VI.

The art of the apothecary was developing rapidly in Britain as well as on the continent during this period. With this development there naturally was created a desire on the part of the pharmacists for a guild of their own, and for a severance of ties with the less well-trained and unsympathetic grocers and spice dealers.

The Society of Apothecaries of London was first created in 1606, when a charter was issued them by the first Stuart King of England, James I (James VI of Scotland). However, this charter was limited, and the society was still jurisdictionally connected with the guild of Grocers.

There is evidence that this move had been preceded by many years of growing dissension, bitterness, charges, countercharges, and political maneuvering, which was not ended by the half-measure of this charter. The pharmacists evidently continued their efforts to secure recognition as an independent profession, receiving assistance from the king's court physicians, Theodore de Mayerne and Henry Atkins (who also fathered the *London Pharmacopoeia*, published in 1618) and from Gideon de Laune, apothecary to the Queen. King James was a man not easily approached; therefore, the apothecaries had to lean heavily on the influence of these intercessors with acceptance at court. Francis Bacon, famous statesman, philosopher and advocate of scientific experimentation,

THE SOCIETY OF APOTHECARIES OF LONDON

Trade in drugs and spices was lucrative in the Middle Ages. In the British Isles, it was monopolized by the Guild of Grocers, which had jurisdiction over the apothecaries. After years of effort, the apothecaries found allies among court physicians. King James I, flanked by two "Beefeaters," wore heavily padded attire because of fear of stabbing. Upon persuasion by the philosopher-politician, Francis Bacon, the King granted a charter in 1617 which formed a separate company known as the "Master, Wardens and Society of the Art and Mystery of the Apothecaries of the City of London" over vigorous protests of the grocers. This was the first organization of pharmacists in the Anglo-Saxon world.

69

in his capacity as author of the Charter of the Society of Apothecaries, presented it for final approval to the king, over protests of representatives of the Company of Grocers.

Finally, on December 6, 1617, the King granted the pharmacists a new charter which formed them into a separate company under the name of the "Master, Wardens and Society of the Art and Mystery of the Apothecaries of the City of London." This was the first separately organized group of pharmacists to have official recognition in the Anglo-Saxon world.

Granting of the Charter to the apothecaries probably was not an entirely paternalistic gesture on the part of James I. At the time, the first official pharmaceutical standard for the realm of England, the *Pharmacopoeiae Londonensis*, was almost ready for publication, and the king's physicians were among its prime movers. The work was published the following year. If it was to be given legal power, there had to be a distinct group of craftsmen upon whom use of the Pharmacopoeia was to be obligatory and who could be held responsible. Likewise, in 1618, the new *Dispensatoire Troy Weights* was introduced by law and their use made obligatory for members of the society.

The charter conferred upon the members of the Society of Apothecaries of London the monopoly of keeping an apothecary's shop and rendered it unlawful for the grocers or any persons, "to make or sell, to compound, prepare, give, apply or administer any medicines or medicinable compositions . . . or by any other way to use or exercise the art, faculty, or mystery of an apothecary or any part thereof, within the city of London and the suburbs or within seven miles of the City." The charter simultaneously established an apprenticeship of seven years and an examination "concerning his (the applicant's) knowledge and election of simples and concerning the preparing, dispensing, handling, commixing, and compounding of medicines . . . "

It was undoubtedly the Baconian spirit that prevailed when the grocers tried to have the separation of the apothecaries from the Company of Grocers revoked, and the King refused. James I justified his refusal by stating that grocers were but merchants having no professional skill, while the practice of the apothecary was "a mystery." "Wherefore," said the King, "I think it fitting they should be a corporation of themselves."

In that day, the terms, "art and mystery" held special significance. "Art" referred to the various technics of preparing drugs for administration to the sick; and "mystery" referred to knowledge, the acquisition of which required a long apprenticeship. Thus, the formula, "art and mystery," came into regular use in the indentures by which an apothecary's apprentice was bound to learn his profession. Such indentures were employed widely when new apprentices were brought into Pharmacy until well into the nineteenth century.

WORLD EVENTS AND PHARMACY HISTORY

Dates, persons, and events of significance to the evolution of Pharmacy include:

1878	Nägeli discovered that bacteria are not given off by moist surfaces.
1878	Edison invented platinum wire (incandescent) electric lamp.
1878-79	Welch, Prudden, Sternberg and Salmon introduced bacteriology in United States.
1879	Neisser discovered gonococcus.
1879	Sir William Macewen removed brain tumors.
1879	Hansen and Neisser discovered lepra bacillus.
1879	First chemically standardized pharmaceutical preparation, *Liquor Ergotae Purificatus*, introduced by Parke-Davis.
1879	Max Nitze introduced cystoscopy.
1879	Manson discovered transmission of filariasis by mosquitoes.
1879	Billings and Fletcher started *Index Medicus*.
1880	Pasteur discovered streptococcus, staphylococcus, and pneumococcus (Sternberg).
1880	Albert Ladenburg, German chemist, isolated hyoscine.
1880	Aseptic surgical techniques developed.
1880	Eberth isolated typhoid bacillus.
1880	Charcot published studies on lesions of the brain.
1880	Pasteur and Sternberg demonstrated carriage of pneumonia bacillus in healthy mouth.
1880	American Surgical Association founded.
1880-81	Laveran discovered parasite of malarial fever.
1881	Ogston discovered staphylococci in abscesses.
1881	Pasteur produced vaccine against anthrax.
1881	Medin discovered epidemic nature of poliomyelitis.
1881	Koch introduced gelatin media (solid plate cultures) and steam sterilization.
1881	Grimaux obtained codeine from morphine.
1881	Carlos Finlay surmised transmission of yellow fever by *Stegomyia fasciata*.

LOUIS HÉBERT, APOTHECARY TO NEW FRANCE (CANADA)

NOWHERE is the intrepid spirit of self-sacrifice and service to fellowmen which has marked the lives of many pharmaceutical pioneers better exemplified than in the life of Louis Hébert—first pharmacist in Canada, and probably the first to practice his profession on the North American continent.

Son of the apothecary to Queen Catherine de Medici, Louis was born in Paris around 1575, and himself became an apothecary. To the little shop on the banks of the Seine came bearers of thrilling tales of a great, rich, savage new world beyond the seas, and they planted the seeds of adventure in the blood of the young Frenchman. Since 1535, when Jacques Cartier sailed up the St. Lawrence, New France had been visited by explorers, fur traders and missionaries—but attempts at settlement had failed. Therefore, when, in 1604, Sieur de Monts set about recruiting a company to establish a permanent colony, Apothecary Louis Hébert was one of those who joined the adventurous group. Others in the expedition included Samuel de Champlain, famous explorer and Chief Geographer to Henry IV of France, and the Baron de Poutrincourt.

The expedition sailed a stormy course, and settled finally at Port Royal, at what is now Lower Granville on the north shore of the Annapolis Basin in western Nova Scotia, across from which stands the present city of Annapolis Royal. Here, in 1605, de Monts' company built the Habitation on a site selected by Champlain and from plans which he drew. The Habitation comprised a group of buildings arranged around a courtyard in the manner of 16th-century farms in northern France, fortified at the two southerly corners by cannons on platforms, and stockades. Occupied from 1605 to 1613, the Habitation of Port Royal antedated the English settlement of Jamestown by two years, the

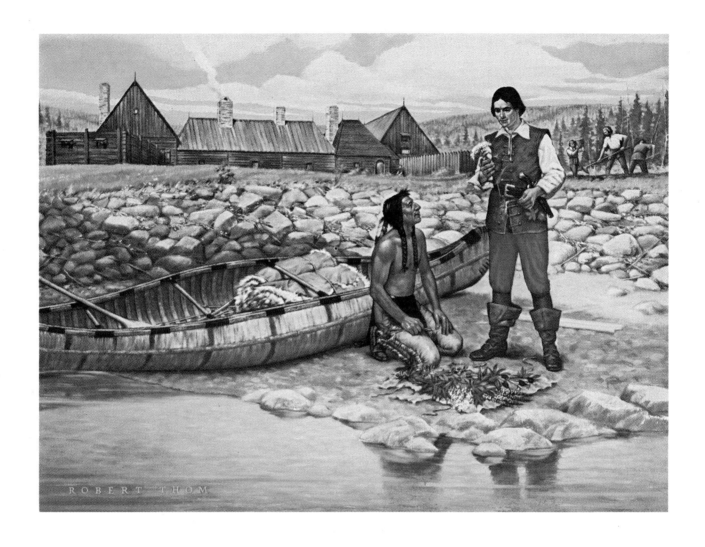

ROBERT THOM

LOUIS HÉBERT, APOTHECARY TO NEW FRANCE (CANADA)

Young Parisian Apothecary Louis Hébert answered the call of the New World in 1605, when he helped de Monts and Champlain build New France's first settlement, the Habitation, at Port Royal (Nova Scotia, Canada). Hébert looked after the health of the pioneers, cultivated native drug plants, and supervised the gardens. At the waterfront, he examined specimens of drug plants offered by friendly Micmac Indians. These included Eupatorium (Boneset), Verbascum (Mullein), Arum, (Jack-in-the-Pulpit), and Hydrastis (Golden Seal). When the Habitation was destroyed by the English in 1613, he returned to his Parisian apothecary shop. The lure of Canada was strong, however, and in 1617, he and his family returned with Champlain to Quebec, where Hébert's "green thumb" gained him lasting fame as the first successful farmer in what is now Canada.

founding of Quebec by three, and the arrival of the Pilgrims at Plymouth by fifteen years.

It was at the Habitation that Hébert's worth for his professional knowledge of pharmacy, and for his avocation, agriculture, was recognized. In *Champlain—The Life of Fortitude*, by Morris Bishop, it is mentioned that "The spring came . . . everyone, gentleman and commoner, cleared the gardens and sowed his seeds, and the virgin soil responded gratefully. The Paris Apothecary Louis Hébert showed a singular love of the soil and gentle power over it. He also sought the woodland herbs and tried to find their medicinal properties . . .

"The Héberts loved the soil and its fruits and wonders; Canada spoiled them for a life of compounding drugs in a sunless Paris shop."

Life on the new continent was rugged. Hébert is reported to have returned to France with a group in 1607, but he came back to Port Royal with Champlain in 1610. With him on this second trip, according to some historians, came Madame Hébert, thus credited to have been the first white woman to have set foot in Canada. During the next few years, Hébert's fame for his medical knowledge and skill, and his stature in the settlement grew until, at one period, he served as acting governor of Port Royal.

Hébert's importance in the Port Royal Colony is further attested by the fact that Bear Island, in the Annapolis Basin, and the Bear River flowing into it, have their names as contractions of "Hébert Island" and "Hébert River"—the names by which they were first designated.

The settlement at Port Royal was fated to have a short life, however, for it was sacked and destroyed by the English from Virginia under Argall in 1613. With the remnants of the colony, the Héberts returned to Paris and reopened the apothecary shop on the Seine.

The Habitation in recent years has been authentically restored on the foundations of Champlain's original site, nestling at the foot of low hills beyond which lies the Bay of Fundy.

But Hébert's roots in Canada were not to wither, and he was to win lasting fame in the new land—not as a pharmacist, but as a farmer. In 1617, Champlain again persuaded Hébert to emigrate with his family, this time with a company going to Quebec, on the shores of the great St. Lawrence River. Hébert signed agreements to provide free medical attention to the settlers and employees of the *Compagnie des Marchands* (Association of Merchants), but he was enjoined from entering into trade either with natives or colonists—so his days in an apothecary shop were ended.

At Quebec, he established Canada's first farm, and gained fame for his agricultural pursuits and studies of native plants.

Louis Hébert's work, which, as Champlain noted, was largely "for others, and not for himself," ended some ten years after he settled in Quebec, as a result of an accident which caused his death.

A monument honoring Hébert's agricultural services to his fellow colonists was erected on occasion of the tercentenary of his settlement in Quebec and stands in a public square in the old city. His Canadian colleagues commemorated his pharmaceutical activities with a tablet, unveiled in 1913, in the historical museum at Annapolis Royal, Nova Scotia, where it may be seen today.

THE GOVERNOR WHO
HEALED THE SICK

For THE first hundred years of Colonial America, pharmaceutical and medical service such as was available, largely was provided by three types of individuals—the governors, the churchmen, and the educators. As always in primitive and pioneer society, preparation of drug substances and remedial measures, as well as their application, were undertaken to a large extent by individual housewives.

The beginning of the seventeenth century saw much restlessness and discontent among European people, especially in England. In addition to intolerable conditions, both economic and religious, the more venturesome among the great trading corporations were casting their eyes toward potentials of the raw new lands across the Atlantic. From the adventurous and the oppressed they recruited strange companies and shipped them to the unknown shores, there to attempt to wrest a toe hold. To the individuals, freedom and economic betterment were held out as glittering goals. From the fruits of their struggles the corporations hoped to reap profits.

Encouraged by liberal charter terms offered by various sponsoring companies, many persons "of quality and wealth, particularly those who were non-conformists in religion," were attracted to the possibilities of the new colonies. Among the early leaders to have come from this group was John Winthrop.

On June 12, 1630, the *Arabella*, flagship of a little fleet from England bearing a group known as the Massachusetts Bay Company, and headed by Governor John Winthrop, dropped anchor near the settlement of Salem, established some two years earlier. The Salem colony was barely able to take care of its own survivors, so many of Winthrop's group moved on to establish the town of Charles. Hardship and suffering were intense; food was scarce;

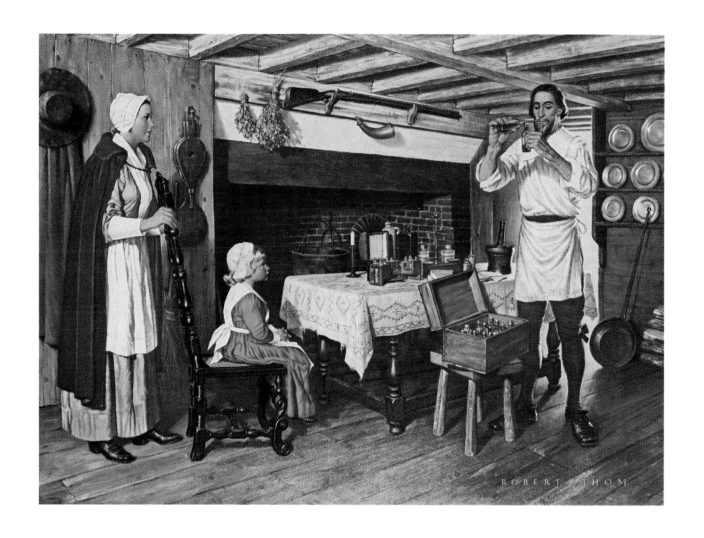

THE GOVERNOR WHO HEALED THE SICK

Many Europeans "of quality and wealth, particularly those who were non-conformists in religion" were attracted to the possibilities of the American Colonies. From Britain came John Winthrop, first Governor of Massachusetts Bay Colony and founder of Boston. Governor Winthrop, unable to induce professionals to the Colony, sought advice from English apothecaries and physicians, and added to his small store of imported drugs those derived from plants native to New England. In his home (about 1640), he made available as best he could the "art and mystery" of the apothecary for his citizens.

scurvy and smallpox prevalent. Deaths were a daily occurrence. Finally, lack of water caused this group of colonists to establish headquarters on the Shawmut peninsula, to which the name of Boston was given.

From Winthrop's *Journal*, begun in 1629, much may be learned about ways of preparation of drugs and administration of medicines in colonial times. Those who could afford to, brought from the homelands small chests of favorite remedies. Native plants to which healing powers were attributed grew in abundance in the New England swamps, woods and hillsides. From the Indians the colonists learned much, too, that helped them through trying days. The Indians, says Bradley, "until cheated and robbed and hounded by religious zealots . . . were friendly with the whites . . . they helped the settlers get acclimated, gave them food when they lacked it, showed them, in their desperate want of doctors and pharmacists, how to heal themselves. And if there was much magic mixed with their medicine, the colonists knew enough to take the medicine and let the magic go."

Despite these measures, there must have been a pressing need for pharmaceutical and medical help that could not be satisfied by the settlers and their wives. The responsibility fell upon Winthrop as their Governor. Being unable to persuade English professionals experienced in the healing arts to come to the New World, Winthrop turned to correspondence to seek advice from his English friends. In 1643 Winthrop received from Edward Stafford, London, a list of "Receipts to Cure Various Disorders," consisting of some eight and one-half pages, referring to some fifty herbs and drugs, among them, toads and frogs burnt to ash and used as "black powder" inwardly and outwardly. Most of the material was of household character and taken from the *Herball* of John Gerard, the second edition of which was published in 1636, prepared by Thomas Johnson, "Citizen and Apothecary of London." The "Receipts" compiled by Stafford were supposed to cure, or at least mitigate plague, smallpox, scurvy, all sorts of fevers, poisons, madness, epilepsy, hysteria, lethargy, vertigo, dysentery, jaundice, pains (rheumatic or others), affections of the urinary organs, pleurisies, watery humors or dropsies, phlegm, catarrhal affections, fractures, dislocations, wounds, bites of venomous creatures, boils, ulcers, gangrene, scrofula, and burns.

Winthrop evidently used his knowledge to obtain, preserve and process supplies for medical use from the surrounding fields; and, when possible, to secure precious drugs from England. That his services were widely known may be deduced from his correspondence. His home was a focal point for those suffering illness in the community. From his chests of priceless imports, and from herbs dried over his mantle, Winthrop prepared medicines as best he could. To his colonists, the good Governor was both apothecary and physician—the only one available west of the Atlantic.

The good Governor's influence extended even further. His gifted son, John Winthrop, Jr., carried on the traditions, both of medicine and of leadership. In addition to practicing medicine, the younger Winthrop (1606-1676) served many years as Governor of Connecticut Colony.

Thus, at a time when the New World was without trained pharmacists and physicians, two pioneers, father and son, sought expert advice and extended as best they could the "art and mystery" of the apothecary and of the physician to the fellow men whom it also was their responsibility to govern.

THE MARSHALL APOTHECARY
AN AMERICAN DYNASTY

PHARMACY in North America owes no small debt to Christopher Marshall (1709-1797) and his family for the development of the ideals of the profession in the New World, and for passing them on to the generations that followed.

Established in Philadelphia early in the eighteenth century, the Marshall Apothecary in ninety-six years that followed (1729-1825) was to become one of the pioneer professional pharmaceutical enterprises in North America; one of the nuclei from which large-scale chemical and pharmaceutical manufacturing sprang; one of the earliest "practical schools" for training of pharmacists; the springboard from which America's first College of Pharmacy was launched; and, last but by no means least, the center of activity of the first known American woman pharmacist.

An immigrant from Dublin, Ireland, Christopher Marshall established himself in the drug business in Philadelphia in 1729 in a rented locality, which was succeeded in 1735 by an expanded establishment in property owned by Marshall. Not only was he prominent in his professional activities, but also in the affairs of the steadily growing "City of Brotherly Love," in the War of Independence, and in the fledgling nation which grew out of that war.

The ideals—social, civic, and professional—which Christopher Marshall developed in his lifetime were conveyed to his two sons, Christopher Marshall, Jr., (1740-1806) and Charles Marshall (1744-1825), and to certain of their progeny. That these seeds were well nourished and planted deeply is reflected in the fame and recognition that these sons achieved, each in his own right, with the family apothecary shop as the cornerstone and background from which they drew both inspiration and sustenance.

In 1765, Christopher Marshall made his sons his partners. When he withdrew from active participation in the Marshall Apothecary

THE MARSHALL APOTHECARY

Christopher Marshall, Irish immigrant, established his apothecary shop in Phila-delphia in 1729. During the next 96 years, this pioneer pharmaceutical enterprise became a leading retail store, nucleus of large-scale chemical manufacturing; a "practical" training school for pharmacists; an important supply depot during the Revolution; and finally, it was managed by granddaughter Elizabeth, America's first woman pharmacist. Christopher earned the title, "The fighting Quaker," dur-ing the Revolution; his sons, Charles and Christopher, Jr., (shown as youths with their father, about 1754) earned individual fame and carried on his fine traditions.

in 1772, his traditions were carried on. It was especially Charles Marshall, as manager of the store (Christopher, Jr., confined his attention mainly to the shipping business) who was responsible for the continuation of these traditions, and for enlarging their application. The Marshall store became, in addition to its role in serving the public, a kind of pharmaceutical educational institution. "Alert and capable young men stood behind the counters and worked in the back room mixing medicines. From six to twelve of these were constantly employed and the store was a practical school from which not a few of the city's ablest druggists and apothecaries of the time were graduated."

Charles Marshall also became the first president (1821-1824) of the Philadelphia College of Pharmacy. This was a further extension of the sound basic tradition of passing on knowledge of the science and art of Pharmacy to worthy young people. Some years later, another president of the college, Daniel B. Smith, was to comment on Charles Marshall as follows:

"Not thirty years ago almost the only apothecary's shop in Philadelphia, where the physician was sure of obtaining the latest foreign preparations, of having his medicines and prescriptions prepared under the eye of the master, and with competent pharmaceutic skill, or in which a strict system of accountability was carried through the details of the shop, was that of the late Charles Marshall. The cause of his success in business was his strict integrity, his scrupulous accuracy and his patient attention."

The firm, under the guidance of Christopher, Jr., and Charles Marshall, was to become one of the first private enterprises in America to begin large-scale manufacture of chemicals. During the War of Independence, the firm supplied large quantities of medicines to Colonial troops. Those of Pennsylvania, New Jersey, Maryland, Delaware, and Virginia obtained their medical supplies almost entirely from this store. As early as 1786, the Marshalls made large quantities of ammonium chloride and Glauber's salt and other chemicals in their laboratory.

The elder Christopher Marshall, though having relinquished his activity in the apothecary, was none the less active in other interests. He became well known in later years for his attitude during the War of Independence, which earned him the cognomen of "the fighting Quaker," as the following record indicates:

"Christopher Marshall, who had long conducted an apothecary shop which enjoyed the confidence of the physicians in an unusual degree, was one of the picturesque figures of the Revolution on the patriot side, though his membership in the Society of Friends forbade warlike activities. It was on this account that he joined the Wetherills (a Quaker family that went into the drug business in the later eighteenth century) in founding the Free Quaker Meeting. In 1776, he was commissioned 'to look after the needs of the sick and wounded in the hospitals of Philadelphia.' "

Charles Marshall retired from active participation in the business in 1801—but within three years, under the management of Charles Marshall's son, "the firm became insolvent by lending its endorsement," or, as another biographer stated it, "through imprudence." It was in 1804 that Charles' daughter, Elizabeth Marshall, a granddaughter of the founder, took over management of the business. A woman of singular good taste and business ability, she "took the shattered business in hand and built it up with great success, supporting the family and gaining for them a position of independence." The business continued under this first American woman pharmacist until 1825, when it was sold to Charles Ellis and Isaac P. Morris.

THE FIRST HOSPITAL PHARMACY
IN COLONIAL AMERICA

THE UNDEVELOPED character of the North American scene, prior to the War of Independence, is perhaps no better exemplified than by the fact that there was no hospital on Colonial American soil until 1751.

It is particularly significant for American Pharmacy that the first American hospital pharmacist made his appearance only one year later. It is striking that both these new and important steps were due to the clarity of mind and energy of action of the great American to whom not only the country of his birth but the world at large owes so much: Benjamin Franklin.

The beginnings of the Pennsylvania Hospital are described in an article by Dr. Joseph W. England in the *Journal of the American Pharmaceutical Association*:

"The suggestion for its (the Pennsylvania Hospital) founding in Philadelphia, came from Dr. Thomas Bond who sought to obtain subscriptions to build such an institution, but failed. The proposal was a novelty in America, and not being well understood, did not appeal. Dr. Bond then came to Franklin, who immediately took a sympathetic interest in the movement, and mapped out a campaign to secure public support . . ."

According to the Pennsylvania Hospital *Minute Book No. 1*, Thomas Bond and Benjamin Franklin began operation of the hospital in 1751 in a rented house, known as the Kinsey house, "with eight beds and four patients." A shipment of drugs, ordered a year previously from London, arrived, and was much larger and more expensive than expected. Rather than return the overshipment, it was decided to use it to establish a hospital pharmacy,

ROBERT
THOM

FIRST HOSPITAL PHARMACY IN COLONIAL AMERICA

Colonial America's first hospital (Pennsylvania) was established in Philadelphia in 1751; the first Hospital Pharmacy began operations there in 1752, temporarily set up in the Kinsey house, which served until the first hospital building was completed. The ingenuity of Benjamin Franklin was helpful to both. First Hospital Pharmacist was Jonathan Roberts; but it was his successor, John Morgan, whose practice as a hospital pharmacist (1755-56), and whose impact upon Pharmacy and Medicine influenced changes that were to become of great importance to the development of professional pharmacy in North America. First as pharmacist, later as physician, he advocated prescription writing and championed independent practice of the two professions.

which they did in an east back room. A partition was authorized to be built which would afford "shelves with drawers below."

The first permanent unit of the Pennsylvania Hospital was completed in December, 1756, and today forms the east wing of the present structure.

As to the establishment of an apothecary shop in the hospital and the hiring of the first practitioner on American soil to devote himself exclusively to staff pharmaceutical activities, Franklin himself, in his *Account of the Pennsylvania Hospital, from Its Rise to the Beginning of the Fifth Month, Called May, 1754*, writes the following:

"The practitioners charitably supplied the medicines gratis till December, 1752, when the managers, having procured an assortment of drugs from London, opened an apothecary's shop in the hospital, and it being found necessary, appointed an apothecary to attend and make up the medicines daily, according to the prescription, with an allowance of fifteen pounds per annum for his care and trouble, he giving bond, with two sufficient sureties, for the faithful performance of his trust."

It was a protégé of Dr. Bond, a man by the name of Jonathan Roberts, who served as the first hospital apothecary until the spring of 1755. All we know of him is that he did his job faithfully and well. Although his successor, John Morgan, a pupil of Dr. John Redman and a protégé of Benjamin Franklin, held the position for a much shorter time (April, 1755, to May, 1756), his practice as a hospital pharmacist led to results which were to become of great importance to the development of professional pharmacy in the United States.

According to an old paper in the Historical Society of Pennsylvania, John Morgan (1735-1789) was only twenty years old at the time he assumed his duties as staff apothecary at the Pennsylvania Hospital. He is described as being "slight of stature, with small hands and feet, a handsome boyish face, blue eyes, and a proud curve of his lips, a Beau Brummel in dress and manners." In the cramped quarters of the first Pennsylvania Hospital he may have conceived the beginnings of his philosophies regarding Pharmacy and Medicine that were to become so controversial in his later life.

After leaving his post at Pennsylvania Hospital, John Morgan studied medicine. After five years of study and experience in London, Edinburgh, Paris, and Italy, he returned and attempted to persuade American physicians to make the European practice of writing prescriptions "the regular mode of practising physik."

In his *Discourse upon the Institution of Medical Schools in America*, read by Morgan as an introductory lecture at the inauguration, in 1765, of a medical school (the first one in Colonial America) in connection with the College of Philadelphia, he said:

"We must regret that the very different employment of physician, surgeon and apothecary should be promiscuously followed by any one man. They certainly require different talents."

And to the objections that were raised to his idea, Dr. Morgan made the following reply:

"Practitioners in general business never do, or can do, the business of an apothecary in their place themselves. They have apprentices for the purpose. After visiting the sick, do not their apprentices make up their prescriptions? I should ask, is not an apothecary acquainted with the art of compounding and making of medicines as skillful as an apprentice? Is not a man educated in the profession to be trusted in preference to one who is only learning the business?"

The situation in Colonial America was still not ripe for the ideas of the former hospital pharmacist and later physician, and first "professor of the theory and practice of medicine, materia medica, pharmacy and pharmaceutical chemistry" in America. However, as Dr. Joseph Carson has stated in his *History of the Medical Department of the University of Pennsylvania (1869)*:

"The course pursued by Dr. John Morgan may be said to have given the original impulse for the cultivation of the profession of pharmacy (in the United States) and sanctioned its independent existence."

CARL W. SCHEELE—GREATEST OF THE PHARMACIST-CHEMISTS

THE STORY of Carl Wilhelm Scheele is the story of a great chemist—one of the world's greatest, who during his few short years gave to the world discoveries that have brought its peoples incalculable advantages, comforts and wealth; yet who shared in little of these, and who never forgot that he was, first of all, a pharmacist.

But out of his life story there came two other stories of particular significance to Pharmacy and to people whom it serves.

First is the story of the enlightened, encouraging preceptorship, the spirit of those pharmacists to whom was trusted guidance of the great chemist's early life.

Second is the story of the great chemical advances that came from his intimate knowledge of, and indefatigable probing of, the secrets of pharmaceutical substances. All of his investigations and discoveries were made in the Swedish pharmacies in which he worked, first as an apprentice, then as a clerk, and finally as owner of his own pharmacy in the small Swedish town of Köping.

Urdang points out that: "Nothing in the early life of Carl Wilhelm Scheele indicated his later greatness. He was born in the then Swedish city of Stralsund (Pomerania), the seventh child among eleven children of the brewer Joachim Christian Scheele. Two years later his father became bankrupt, and there was no time or money for education of the shy, reserved boy. At the age of 14, he left school and became an apprentice to the apothecary Martin Andreas Bauch, owner of the Pharmacy at the Unicorn in Gothenburg.

"Now the latent talents and energies of the young man began to develop. He found himself surrounded by substances, the real nature of which was not known or incompletely known and which

SCHEELE—GREATEST OF THE PHARMACIST-CHEMISTS

During his few short years, Carl Wilhelm Scheele gave to the world discoveries that have brought its people incalculable advantages. Yet he never forgot that he was, first of all, a pharmacist. Encouraged by enlightened preceptors, all of his discoveries were made in the Swedish pharmacies in which he worked, as apprentice, as clerk, and finally as owner, in Köping. He began in a corner of the stock room of the Unicorn Apothecary in Gothenburg. With rare genius, he made thousands of experiments, discovered oxygen, chlorine, prussic acid, tartaric acid, tungsten, molybdenum, glycerin, nitroglycerin, and countless other organic compounds that enter into today's daily life, industry, health, and comfort.

89

he could investigate and experiment with as he pleased, pushed by no one and responsible only to himself. His master, recognizing the unusual zeal of his apprentice, not only encouraged Scheele's scientific curiosity in granting him the material needed and as much time as possible; but in addition, put his well equipped library at his apprentice's disposal. It was during the eight years of his stay in Gothenburg (1757-1765) and the following three years of clerkship at the Pharmacy at the Spotted Eagle at Malmo (1765-1768) owned by the apothecary Peter Magnus Kjellstrom, that Scheele laid the groundwork for most of the discoveries which made him one of the greatest chemists of all time."

Scheele's youthful experimentation was carried on in an improvised laboratory in a corner of the stock room under the indulgent eye of preceptor Bauch. Had Apothecaries Bauch and Kjellstrom lacked the foresight to permit young Carl to carry on his ceaseless experimenting; had they been more insistent that he devote his time to the menial tasks about the store, the world might have lost a great genius.

Anders Jahan Retzius, who became acquainted with Scheele at Malmo and who was the first real scientist to recognize and to take advantage of the genius in the young apothecary clerk, described his young friend in a letter written about 1786 as follows:

"His (Scheele's) genius was given to him exclusively for physical science. He had absolutely no interest in any other. It is doubtless for this reason that his talents seemed to be poor if other matters were concerned. His memory was excellent. However, this too seemed only fitted to retain matters relating to chemistry . . . He made all kinds of experiments, so to say, pell-mell. This taught him what many a doctrinaire could never learn: since working by no formulated principles he observed much and discovered much that the doctrinaire would consider impossible, inasmuch as it was opposed to his theories."

At the age of thirty-two, while still an apothecary clerk who had yet to take his Swedish apothecary examination, Scheele was made a member of the Swedish Royal Academy of Science—the highest distinction his country had to offer.

90

The authority which Scheele enjoyed was so great, and his honesty and simplicity of character so obvious and disarming, that none of the usual scientific jealousies and quarrels ever touched him. When his book on air and fire, due to the negligence of his publisher, appeared so late that some of his statements concerning oxygen were in the meantime made and published by other authors, nobody dared to raise the question of plagiarism.

Until his early death at the age of only forty-three years, Scheele reported one discovery and observation after the other in such a rapid succession that his contemporaries were almost overwhelmed. So exclusively devoted was he to his science on the one hand and to his pharmaceutical service to his fellow citizens on the other that he literally had no private life.

The profit drawn by a peaceful world from the discoveries of Apothecary Scheele has been enormous. The work of this "corner pharmacist" has become foundational in the edifice of modern civilization. The bleaching and the laundry industry and wide fields of chemical disinfection, among them that of water purification, are inconceivable without chlorine. The fruit acids discovered by Scheele are of highest importance for the modern foodstuff and beverage industries. Tungsten and molybdenum, to the discovery of which Scheele paved the way, are indispensable in modern steel industry; and glycerin enters into many of our daily-life commodities used for a multitude of purposes and in many industries. Great creativeness, as well as great destruction, came from the application of Scheele's findings to nitroglycerin and the explosives industry.

Perhaps the most perfect tribute was paid him in 1892, at the time of the creation of a monument in Stockholm, when it was said publicly that "Scheele contributed more to the development of the era in which we are living than diplomatic negotiations and pitched battles."

ANDREW CRAIGIE—AMERICA'S FIRST APOTHECARY GENERAL

THE CONTROVERSY over the status of pharmacists in the armed services of the United States (about which many bitter political battles were fought, won, and lost, during the second quarter of the twentieth century) seems to have been older than the nation itself. Though pharmaceutical service to the military has vastly improved over 180 years, acknowledgment of the pharmacist's professional position by the fighting forces has had many ups and downs.

The first man to hold the rank of a commissioned pharmaceutical officer in an American army was the Bostonian, Andrew Craigie, son of a shipmaker of the same name. Records do not indicate his education beyond Boston Latin School, or where he got his early pharmaceutical training. Even the date of his birth is controversial, having been variously recorded by historians as June 7, 1743, June 6, 1744, and February 22, 1754. The latter date seems most plausible, based on the explanation of Frederick Haven Pratt, in *The Craigies*. This author claims that Captain Andrew Craigie had two sons, both of whom he named Andrew— the first died in infancy; the second, born some ten years later, also bore his father's name. Due to the casualness of records in those days, birth dates of the Craigie brothers named Andrew often were confused. Records agree that the surviving brother died September 19, 1819, of apoplexy.

Young Craigie must have been an apothecary of some standing and promise, however, (his title of Doctor was only a courtesy) for he was appointed commissary of medical stores by the Committee of Safety of the Province of Massachusetts, April 30, 1775. On May 14, Craigie was "directed to impress beds, bedding and other necessities for the sick."

A. CRAIGIE—AMERICA'S FIRST APOTHECARY GENERAL

First man to hold the rank of a commissioned pharmaceutical officer in an American army was the Bostonian apothecary, Andrew Craigie. First appointed commissary of medical stores by Massachusetts' Committee of Safety, April 30, 1775, he was present at the Battle of Bunker Hill, June 17, 1775, and probably assisted in taking care of the sick and wounded there in a makeshift station back of the lines. When Congress reorganized the Medical Department of the Army in 1777, Craigie became the first Apothecary General. His duties included procurement, storage, manufacture, and distribution of the Army's drug requirements. He also developed an early wholesaling and manufacturing business.

It is generally believed that Andrew Craigie was present at the Battle of Bunker Hill (actually fought on Breed's Hill), June 17, 1775, and gained his first experience in taking care of the sick and wounded there, assisting Dr. D. Townsend. The supply of medicines at this time was deplorably low, only a few scattered medicine chests being available, and some of these had been impressed into service from private homes. Dr. Benjamin Church was ranking medical officer and Craigie's department superior at this time.

Other illustrious patriots were engaged in the Battle of Bunker Hill. The troops were commanded by Colonel William Prescott, grandfather of Albert B. Prescott, who was to profoundly reshape pharmaceutical education a century later. Dr. Joseph Warren, named a major general three days before, refused command because of inexperience, but lost his life in the battle. His younger brother, John Warren, founded Harvard Medical School; and John's son, John Collins Warren, was the first surgeon to perform an operation under anesthesia, in Boston, in 1846.

The following month, July 4, 1775, the Massachusetts Provincial Congress appointed Andrew Craigie to be "medical commissary and apothecary to the army raised by this Congress." Although restricted to Massachusetts Province, it was the first official appointment of an army apothecary in America. Craigie served in this capacity during the siege of Boston. His compensation was five pounds a month.

There is record only of the highlights of Andrew Craigie's military career from this point on. On July 17, 1775, the Continental Congress created the position of an Apothecary on the staff of each army hospital, the appointment being left to the respective "director-general and chief physician." When, on April 7, 1777, Congress passed a resolution effecting the reorganization of the Medical Department of the Army, the position of Apothecary General (with the rank of Lieutenant Colonel) was created and Andrew Craigie was the first and most important of those appointed. The duties, as outlined in the resolution, were: "That there be one apothecary general for each district, whose duty it shall be to receive, prepare, and deliver medicines and

94

other articles of his department to the hospitals and army, as shall be ordered by the director general . . .''

A further reorganization of the military medical department by Congress took place October 6, 1780, abolishing the district departments and concentrating authority in one medical staff. The title, Apothecary General, borne by several persons of equal rank, disappeared. One Apothecary and five assistants were appointed. Andrew Craigie became this Apothecary and kept his position until 1783.

That Craigie was efficient in fulfillment of his duties, as well as at making friends, is borne out by a letter written by General George Washington to an influential member of Congress recommending Craigie for the appointment. To his credit also was that in 1778 he suggested and put into practice the establishment of general laboratories and storehouses to serve the medical needs of the army. This is confirmed by a later report that "Hospital drugs were prepared and compounded mostly in Apothecary General Craigie's shop at Carlisle, Pennsylvania." Thus Craigie is said to be the first officially recognized manufacturer of pharmaceutical products on a large scale in America.

Apothecary Craigie's talents ran in other directions, too. According to Lyman F. Kebler, in the *Dictionary of American Biography*, "During his service in the Revolutionary army, Craigie acquired a large fortune, buying up government promissory certificates and other speculations . . ." also, "He was a modern wholesale druggist a century ahead of his time."

At the close of the revolutionary war, Craigie returned to Boston and began speculation in land. He bought the well-known Craigie House in 1792, which later became famous as the home of Henry Wadsworth Longfellow.

The end of the spectacular career of America's first Apothecary General is clothed in nearly as much confusion as its beginning. One biographer says that "After a time, his glory waned and he became so heavily involved in debt that he was unable to leave his property for fear of arrest." Another source states that the skill and resourcefulness that served his country so well led him to financial and social success.

SERTÜRNER—FIRST OF THE ALKALOID CHEMISTS

THROUGHOUT countless centuries, untold thousands of suffering humans found much needed relief from pain and agony in the inspissated juice of the opium poppy. Administration of crude, nonstandard opium, however, was not without its disadvantages and disasters.

The dream of isolating the essential, or specifically effective, constituents from plant material had, since the days of Paracelsus, occupied the minds and hands of researchers in Pharmacy. The great Swedish pharmacist Scheele had paved the way by isolating one organic plant acid after another in his laboratories in back rooms of apothecary shops—but still the secret of the sleep-producing power of opium resisted solution.

It remained for a young German drug clerk, hardly having finished his five years of apprenticeship, to probe opium's secrets; and not only to give the world opium's chief narcotic principle, morphine, but simultaneously to fully recognize the importance of what he had done. His name was Friedrich Wilhelm Adam Sertürner.

Again, the back room of an apothecary shop was the scene of research of world-wide importance. Sertürner started his experiments with opium in 1803 in the Hof-Apotheke in Paderborn, Germany. In 1805 he reported the results of his first investigations to the famous pharmacist-chemist and editor of the *Journal der Pharmacie*, Johan Bartholomaüs Trommsdorff, who, though expressing doubts, published them. While these early reports dealt primarily with the discovery of meconic acid, Sertürner announced, in a more detailed paper in the same journal in 1806, his isolation of the narcotic principle of opium, which he called *principium somni-*

SERTÜRNER—FIRST OF THE ALKALOID CHEMISTS

Swedish pharmacist Scheele paved the way for isolating organic plant acids; but it remained for a young German apothecary, Friedrich Wilhelm Adam Sertürner, to give the world opium's chief narcotic principle, morphine; and to recognize and prove the importance of a new class of organic substances: alkaloids. His first announcements challenged, Sertürner in 1816 conducted a new series of bold, startling experiments in his apothecary shop in Einbeck, including a series of physiologic tests on himself and three young friends. Recognition and fame followed. Relocating in an apothecary shop in Hameln, Sertürner continued organic chemical experimentation and discovery throughout his life.

97

ferum. Simultaneously he announced what proved to be of almost greater importance than the isolation of morphine: this new substance was alkaline in nature, hence was the first representative of a new class of organic bases which were "salifyable," that is, they formed salts with organic as well as with inorganic acids. Fifty-seven experiments had been designed and carried through by young Sertürner before he made his daring conclusions.

Remarkable as were these twin discoveries, it is equally remarkable how completely this young pharmacist, then 23 years of age, grasped the importance of his discovery, being aware not only that he had isolated a hitherto unknown and most valuable substance, but also had initiated a new field of research. Another pharmacist, Karl Friedrich Wilhelm Meissner, in 1818, coined the name for this field—alkaloid (substances with alkali-like behavior) chemistry.

Reaction of the scientific world to Sertürner's findings was not encouraging. Typically, there were scoffers and detractors. The French pharmacist-chemist Derosne was claimed to have discovered morphine shortly before Sertürner, but this was later disproved.

Meantime, young Sertürner, at the age of 26, had become the owner of an apothecary shop in Einbeck. He continued his experiments, and the publication of his results, fighting back at those who questioned his achievements. Finally, in 1817, he published a mature and conclusive re-evaluation of his former findings, plus an account of new, bold, startling experiments further proving his contentions. In Gilbert's *Annalen der Physik*, Sertürner published his "On Morphine, a New Salifyable Base, and Meconic Acid, Regarded as the Principal Constituents of Opium." Here for the first time there appears the name, morphine (*Morphium*, derived from *Morpheus*, the Greek god of dreams). In this paper, Sertürner dared the statement that probably the new substance contained not only oxygen, carbon, and hydrogen, but also nitrogen. Finally, he presented the results of physiologic experiments to which he, himself, and three other young men had subjected themselves. In the course of forty-five minutes, each of the four human guinea pigs took three half-grain doses of morphine. This certainly was an overdose, and must have caused them considerable incon-

98

venience. But the effect of morphine was proved, and after a few days no harmful consequences could be observed.

Reviewing his previous work, Sertürner—who signed his paper as "Pharmacist at Einbeck in the Kingdom of Hanover"—did not hesitate to punch holes in Derosne's methods. Accompanied by an appreciative comment by Editor Gilbert, this publication received the attention denied its predecessors. The first to recognize and acknowledge Sertürner's discovery was the French chemist-physicist, Gay-Lussac, then at the height of his fame. He presented the French-speaking world a translation (prepared by the pharmacist-chemist Robiquet).

Now that the ice was broken, honors came to Sertürner. In 1817, he was distinguished with membership in the Society for Mineralogy at Jena, presided over by no less person than the great German sage, Goethe, and received a Doctor's degree from the University of Jena. In rapid sequence other scientific societies bestowed membership on him.

The detractors still were busy. The French pharmacist-chemist Vauquelin claimed the discovery of morphine for the Frenchman, Seguin, and accused Sertürner of plagiarism. However, in 1831, the Institut de France awarded Sertürner the coveted Monthyon prize for "having recognized the alkaline nature of morphine and thus having opened an avenue which has led to great medical discoveries."

Sertürner in 1820 became owner of an apothecary shop in Hameln, and in his later years tried a number of new experiments and wrote several books. In spite of sound and sometimes prophetic ideas, his endeavors did not find the appreciation he expected, and Sertürner died in 1841 a disappointed and embittered man.

The memory of this apothecary is honored by tablets in Paderborn, Einbeck, and Hameln, where he practiced his profession, and in Neuhaus, where he was born. His greatest tribute, however, lives in today's highly developed field of alkaloidal chemistry, for which he laid the basis.

CAVENTOU, PELLETIER
AND QUININE

FROM THE TIME that Europeans became aware, late in the eighteenth century, of the value of the Peruvian barks for the alleviation of symptoms of malaria and other intermittent fevers, scientist after scientist had tried to lift the veil from the secret of the effect of cinchona bark. In a memoir published in the *Journal de Pharmacie* in 1818, the pharmacist Lambert listed the names of some 30 chemists, physicians, and pharmacists who had tried their hands in this research.

The German pharmacist Sertürner had pointed the way for further research toward isolation of effective plant constituents by emphasizing the alkali-like character of morphine, the first alkaloid isolated—but the character of his work had been generally overlooked by his French contemporaries until 1817. The question then became: which plants next will be subjected to examination, by whom, and with what success?

The important plants analyzed were, in chronological sequence, *ipecacuanha* (ipecac root), *Strychnos nux vomica* (ignatia bean), and cinchona (Peruvian bark). The results were emetine (1817), strychnine and brucine (1818), and, most important of all, quinine (1820). The successful investigators were two young French pharmacists working together as an ideal research team —Pierre-Joseph Pelletier and Joseph-Bienaimé Caventou. In 1820, Pelletier was 32, and Caventou, 25 years of age. Their experimentations with cinchona barks were carried out in their laboratory in the back of a Parisian apothecary shop.

Despite Sertürner's reports, and those of Scheele before him, the problems studied by Caventou and Pelletier were not easily solved. Each of the plants, or plant parts, presented its individual problems. That held especially true for cinchona bark. In 1811, a

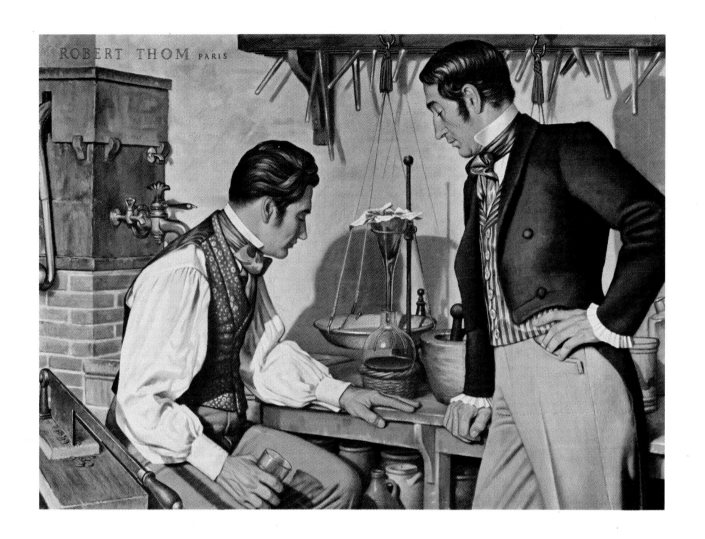

CAVENTOU, PELLETIER AND QUININE

Taking their cue from Sertürner's alkaloidal experiments, two young French pharmacists, Pierre-Joseph Pelletier and Joseph-Bienaimé Caventou, isolated emetine from ipecacuanha in 1817; strychnine and brucine from nux vomica in 1818; then, in their laboratory in the back of a Parisian apothecary shop, they tackled the problem that had baffled scientists for decades—wresting the secrets of the Peruvian barks that were so useful against malaria. In 1820 Caventou and Pelletier announced the methods for separation of quinine and cinchonine from the cinchona barks; prepared pure salts, had them tested clinically, and set up manufacturing facilities. Many other discoveries came from their pharmacy-laboratory, and high honors were accorded them.

Portuguese physician, B. A. Gomez, had isolated a substance from gray cinchona bark (*Cinchona condamina*). However, he did not attribute the essential effects of cinchona bark to it.

Pelletier and Caventou repeated Gomez' work with improved methods and obtained, for the first time, pure cinchonine. This product was alkaline in its reaction, and it was effective. Had the two researchers stopped here, quinine, the most effective alkaloid of cinchona bark, would still have had to await discovery. Fortunately, they did not. They started the examination of the barks of other cinchona species, first that of yellow cinchona bark (*Cinchona cordifolia*), and finally that of red cinchona bark (*Cinchona oblongifolia*). The result was described by the two investigators:

"We are convinced that this effective principle is the salifyable base: the cinchonine in the gray cinchona, the quinine in the yellow cinchona, and both substances in the red cinchona."

With that, the discovery of quinine was announced.

A method for the separation of cinchonine and quinine was designed; salts of both alkaloids were prepared; and after the work done was examined by three of the best contemporary French chemists (Vauquelin, Deycux, and Thenard), Pelletier presented the report compiled jointly by Caventou and himself to the Parisian Academy of Science in two lectures, given on September 11, and October 16, 1820. The manuscript still is preserved in the archives of the Academy. It covers sixty-one pages and is entitled, *Recherches chimiques sur quelques plantes de la famille des Rubiacées. Premier mémoire sur les quinquinas.* It has been agreed that the sessions of the Academy in which Pelletier read this *mémoire* were among the best attended and were considered as most memorable.

As soon as they had isolated cinchonine and quinine and prepared a series of salts, Pelletier and Caventou submitted these substances to the best Parisian physicians, among them the famous physiologist, Magendie, for clinical testing. The results, proving the superiority of sulfate of quinine over all other products, were most satisfying, establishing quinine as the supreme drug for all kinds of intermittent fevers.

Well aware of the commercial possibilities of the discovery,

Pelletier did not lose any time in starting the large-scale manufacturing of quinine. But in making known his methods of preparation of quinine, and especially of its sulfate, he refused, for the sake of mankind, to exploit this discovery as a monopoly. Soon the manufacture of quinine required greater facilities than could be offered in the back room laboratory of Pelletier's pharmacy. A separate plant was established, which, after various changes of domicile and name, is still in operation. In a few years the production of quinine was taken up all over the world. In the United States, the firm of Farr and Kunzi, in Philadelphia, manufactured quinine as early as 1822. One year later, in 1823, Rosengarten and Sons, in Philadelphia, commenced the manufacture of quinine sulfate.

The research activities of this pair of pharmacists did not stop with their success with quinine. They went on, as a team, individually, and in collaboration with others, to further discoveries; but it is for quinine that they are best remembered.

The work of Pelletier and Caventou, both sons of prominent pharmacists and themselves retail pharmacists as well as researchers and teachers, has found the recognition which it so amply deserved. In 1827 they were awarded the *Prix Monthyon*, and in 1900 a monument was erected in their honor in Paris, paid for by contributions from all over the world and showing the two savants in full figure on the same pedestal, dressed in their academic gowns. Speaking on the occasion of the unveiling of the monument, another famous pharmacist, the discoverer of fluorine, Henri Moissan, expressed the conviction that now the men to whom the world is indebted for quinine have achieved the "immortality of bronze." However, in 1941, the Nazis hauled down the statues and melted them. Again, in 1951, public contributions brought about the erection of a new, simpler monument in their honor.

AMERICAN PHARMACY
BUILDS ITS FOUNDATIONS

A SIGNIFICANT QUALITY of democratic procedure is that out of adversity there have arisen many of our soundest traditions and institutions. This operating principle of democracy; this spirit of "let's do something about it," was to serve the profession of Pharmacy well in America. It found its first application during 1821 in the founding of America's first association of pharmacists, The Philadelphia College of Pharmacy, and the organization of the first school of pharmacy on the North American continent as an integral part of the College. (At this period, the term "college" was used to designate an association, as well as an institution of learning.)

It was a dilemma that early in 1821 stimulated the pharmacists of Philadelphia, then America's largest city, to bind themselves together in a professional body, to determine rules for their own conduct, and to establish an educational institution to be operated under their own supervision.

First problem was the low state of the general level of dispensing of drugs and medicines. The most ignorant tradesman might compete with the most scrupulous apothecary. Inferior, deteriorated drugs competed against the choicest and most select; and price cutting was a common commercial weapon—even in this early day.

Second problem, and the one that aroused the Philadelphia pharmacists to the boiling point, was the actions of Dr. John Redman Coxe, dean of the medical faculty of the University of Pennsylvania. Dr. Coxe publicly deplored the state of Pharmacy in the city, and goaded the Board of Trustees of the University to adopt and publish resolutions establishing a degree of Master of Pharmacy. In addition to being available to students who would take the courses of lectures contemplated by the University, this degree was to be conferred upon a number of apothecaries of the

ROBERT THOM

AMERICAN PHARMACY BUILDS ITS FOUNDATIONS

Faced with two major threats: deterioration of the practice of pharmacy, and discriminatory classification by the University of Pennsylvania medical faculty, the pharmacists of Philadelphia held a tempestuous protest meeting in Carpenters' Hall, February 23, 1821. At a second meeting, March 13, the pharmacists voted formation of: an association, which became The Philadelphia College of Pharmacy; a self-policing board; and a school of pharmacy. Sixty-eight pharmacists signed the Constitution of the first pharmaceutical association in the United States; by November 9, American Pharmacy's first educational institution, bearing the same name, opened.

105

city of Philadelphia who, in the opinion of the Faculty of Medicine, were "deserving." These resolutions were published in *Poulson's Advertiser*, February 19, 1821.

"The reaction of the druggists and apothecaries* to these resolutions was immediate and pronounced," according to *The First Century of The Philadelphia College of Pharmacy*. Prides were hurt; professional standing was at stake; there was great lack of confidence in Dr. Coxe and his intentions; competence of the Faculty of Medicine to judge fairly was questioned; their presumptuous action was resented.

Henry Troth, a prosperous young Quaker apothecary, and Peter K. Lehman, a drug store proprietor, visited their neighbors and enlisted support in calling a meeting to be held in Carpenters' Hall, February 23, 1821 (four days after publication of the University's resolutions). A leading wholesale druggist, Stephen North, was called to the chair and presided over the meeting. Peter Williamson was chosen as secretary. The discussion was general and very spirited. For some present, it was an awkward situation; they had supported Dr. Coxe's plan. Others viewed the University's plan as "liable to serious objections and inadequate to the attainment of the objects" in view. A committee was appointed to determine whether it might not be "preferable to adopt a plan . . . distinct from the one proposed." The committee was made up of Samuel Jackson, Daniel B. Smith, Robert Milnor, Peter Williamson, Stephen North, Henry Troth, Samuel Biddle, Charles Allen, and Frederick Brown. Significantly, as has been pointed out by Charles H. LaWall, this was "an enterprise of youth." The average age of the committee members about whom there is definite information was but 28 years.

The committee immediately set about its task and made its report to a second meeting of pharmacists, held in Carpenters' Hall, March 13, 1821. While rejecting the proposals of Dr. Coxe

---

*In 1821, "druggist" was the title applied to a person conducting a wholesale drug business; an "apothecary" was a compounder of prescriptions and conducted a retail drug business.

and the University, the committee, in its report, did observe that "This action of the University has had one happy effect . . . it has aroused (the druggists and apothecaries) to a sense of the propriety of placing their business on the respectable footing it ought to

Founders of
The Philadelphia College of Pharmacy

Sixty-eight "druggists and apothecaries" comprised the list of original members of The Philadelphia College of Pharmacy. Our painting represents their first meeting in Carpenters' Hall. Of these, only 10 can be identified in the picture.

1. Stephen North
   (Chairman)
2. Daniel B. Smith
3. Peter Williamson
   (Secretary)
4. Samuel Jackson
5. Peter K. Lehman
6. Henry Troth
7. Charles Marshall, Jr.
8. Charles Marshall
   (First President)
9. John P. Wetherill
10. Samuel Price Wetherill*
    (Chairman, Board of Trustees)

Great-great-uncle of Colonel Samuel Price Wetherill, chairman of the College's 1960 Board of Trustees.

107

possess as a branch of science . . ." However, the committee believed such "desirable and highly important objects" could "only be effectually attained by the interposition and active agency of the druggists and apothecaries themselves."

To "effectuate the reformation" the committee recommended "the establishment of a College (association) of Apothecaries, the attention of which will be constantly directed to the qualities of articles brought into the drug market, in which subjects relating to their business and its objects can be discussed, and information beneficial and interesting to the trade communicated;" and it was proposed to establish a school of pharmacy "in which lectures designed especially for the instruction of druggists and apothecaries should be delivered."

The committee further offered a constitution for such an association for the consideration of the meeting. The constitution was presented and adopted, and signed by those present, who numbered 68—about one half of those identified with Pharmacy in the city and outlying districts. It was agreed that the members would meet four times a year; and there would be sixteen members on the board of trustees. The constitution provided that this board should: "Establish a school of pharmacy, provide suitable apparatus and a library and appoint one or more lecturers as may be deemed expedient, on materia medica, chemistry, and pharmacy, and on such branches of natural science as may be useful in the instruction of an apothecary; appoint a committee of inspection who shall examine all articles of drugs and medicines brought into the market and submitted to them; and appoint a committee of equity to settle any disputes that may arise in the transactions of business by the members of the College which may be referred to them." Membership dues were to be $5 a year; and new members might be admitted if they had been "regularly educated as a druggist or apothecary," or had received a diploma from the College.

First formal meeting of the College took place on March 27, 1821. The dean of Philadelphia's apothecaries, Charles Marshall, though nearly eighty years of age, was chosen president. (This

Charles Marshall was the younger son of Christopher Marshall, founder of the Marshall Apothecary.)

William Lehman and Stephen North were named vice presidents; Daniel B. Smith, secretary, and William Heyl, treasurer. Samuel Price Wetherill became chairman of the Board of Trustees. (His great-great-nephew, Colonel Samuel Price Wetherill, Jr., was, 134 years later, the chairman of the College's Board of Trustees.) Peter Williamson became the Trustees' secretary.

The Board of Trustees leased rooms in the Hall of the German Society for two hundred dollars a year in which lectures might be given, and Dr. Samuel Jackson, a graduate in medicine who had inherited his father's drug business, opened his course of lectures on materia medica and pharmacy on the evening of November 9, 1821. Gerard Troost opened lectures on chemistry the following evening. Lectures were to be given three times a week; tickets to the first course were twelve dollars; for the chemistry course, ten dollars.

The State of Pennsylvania granted a charter to the organization, March 30, 1822, and its name was formally changed from The Philadelphia College of Apothecaries to The Philadelphia College of Pharmacy. For the first time in the United States, the important bearing of the pursuit of the pharmacist upon the general welfare was recognized in a statute book.

Charles Marshall retired from presidency of the College in 1824, and William Lehman advanced to the position. On his death in 1829, the place was taken by Daniel B. Smith, who served in the office for twenty-five years.

Dr. Jackson continued his lectures for six years, being succeeded by Benjamin Ellis. Dr. Troost taught in the College only one year, being succeeded by Dr. George B. Wood. In 1831, Wood transferred to the chair of materia medica and pharmacy, and Franklin Bache was elected to the chair of chemistry—a union of minds which set the school forward so distinctly it achieved an eminent national and international position. Thus, they headed a long list of names illustrious in Pharmacy which were associated with the teaching staff of Philadelphia College of Pharmacy, including

Durand, Carson, Hare, Squibb, Maisch, Procter, Remington, Kraemer, Cook, Newcomb, Sadtler, LaWall, Ryan, Griffith, Tice, Osol, and a host of others.

In 1832, the College acquired a home of its own on Zane Street, where it remained until 1868; it then built its own building on 10th Street. There it remained until 1928, when quarters were occupied at 43rd Street, Kingsessing and Woodland Avenues. Alterations during 1948 to 1950 greatly expanded its facilities.

In 1921, at the time of the College's centennial, the demand for education in the fields of chemistry, bacteriology, and biology was recognized, and its name was changed to The Philadelphia College of Pharmacy and Science.

Not only is The Philadelphia College of Pharmacy and Science the oldest such institution in the United States; it is one of the few still operated on an independent basis, supported by tuition fees and grants from persons interested in its perpetuation. Throughout the years the College has given much to the health professions serving the public, to the literature of Pharmacy, to research, and to the training of teachers as well as practitioners of the profession of Pharmacy. At the conclusion of 144 years of continuous operation, its graduates numbered 13,675.

WORLD EVENTS AND PHARMACY HISTORY

Dates, persons, and events of significance to the evolution of Pharmacy include:

1882   Koch discovered tubercle bacillus.

1882   Löffler and Schütz isolated bacillus of glanders in pure culture.

1882   Max Sänger improved cesarean section.

1882   Liebreich introduced lanolin.

1882   Langenbuch excised the gall-bladder.

1882   Public Health Act (Canada) passed.

1882   Royal Academy of Medicine in Ireland (Dublin) founded.

1882   Royal Society of Canada (Ottawa) founded.

1882   Frank invented process for purifying water by filtration through infusorial silica.

1883   Edwin Klebs discovered diphtheria bacillus.

1883   J. Marion Sims died.

1883   Kjeldahl introduced method of estimating nitrogen.

1883   Golgi introduced silver stain for nerve cells.

1883   Pasteur vaccinated against anthrax.

1883   Metchnikoff stated phagocytic theory of immunity.

1883   Unna introduced ichthyol.

1883   Koch discovered bacilli of cholera and infectious conjunctivitis.

1883   Adolf von Baeyer obtained formula of indigo.

1883   Kühne and Chittenden demonstrated role of trypsin in digestion.

1883   Conner (Cincinnati) performed gastrectomy.

1883   A. F. A. King propounded theory of malarial transmission by mosquitoes.

1883-85   Gustav Neuber (Kiel) introduced aseptic hospital.

1884   Nicolaier discovered tetanus bacillus.

1884   Credé introduced silver nitrate instillations for infantile conjunctivitis.

1884   Ludwig Knorr discovered antipyrine.

1884   Baumann discovered sulphonal (Kast, 1888).

1884   Gaffky obtained pure culture of typhoid bacillus (Eberth, 1880).

1884   Loeffler obtained pure culture of diphtheria bacillus (Klebs, 1883).

1884   Emmerich isolated colon bacillus (Escherich, 1886).

1884   Hueppe investigated lactic acid bacilli in sour milk.

1884   Chamberland invented porcelain bacterial filter.

1884   Mergenthaler introduced linotyping.

1884   United States Bureau of Labor established.

1884   Carl Koller employed cocaine in eye surgery.

1885   Golgi discovered glia cells.

1885   Pasteur developed vaccine against rabies.

1885   Yamanashi isolated ephedrine (Nagai, 1887).

1885   H. H. Rusby made extensive trip through South America, seeking new botanical drugs.

1885   Oscar Loewi discovered bactericidal property of formaldehyde (formalin).

1885   Fraser introduced strophanthus.

1885   Bumm obtained pure cultures of gonococcus.

1885   Halsted introduced conduction anesthesia.

1885-86   Sigmund Freud studied under Charcot at the Salpêtrière.

1886   Von Bergmann introduced steam sterilization in surgery.

1886   Moissan discovered fluorine.

1886   Limousin developed glass ampoules for hypodermic solutions.

1886   Escherich investigated bacteria of intestines in infants.

1886   Fitz described pathology of appendicitis.

1886   Marie connected acromegaly with the pituitary body.

1886   Marcel von Nencki introduced salol.

1886   Soxhlet introduced sterilized milk for nutrition of infants.

1886   Kopp, Cahn, and Hepp introduced acetanilide as antifebrin (Gerhardt, 1843).

1887   Weichselbaum discovered meningococcus.

1887   Gram introduced diuretin.

1887   Kast and Hinsberg introduced phenacetin.

THE SHAKERS AND
MEDICINAL HERBS

THE CONCEPT of the monastery gardens of old: that from God's earth one draws the means to cure human ailments, was reborn among the Protestant sectarians who settled the North American Colonies. Gardens for the cultivation and study of medicinal herbs and plants were to be found early in the 1700's; the first of record near Philadelphia, and others in the Moravian communities near Nazareth and Bethlehem, Pennsylvania. The most unique of these American sectarian ventures into drug plant cultivation, and by far the most important, was undertaken by the Shakers, first at New Lebanon, New York, and later in other Shaker communities.

Begun about 1800, this Shaker enterprise continued for more than 100 years, but reached its peak in the third quarter of the nineteenth century, when more than 248 varieties of plants were collected or cultivated, solid extracts produced by the tons, and the Shakers' reputation for the purity and reliability of their products commanded a market both nationwide and world-wide.

It was in 1774, the year before the start of the War of Independence, that the United Society of Believers in Christ's Second Appearing, commonly known as the Shakers, established its original settlement at Niskeyuna, near Albany, New York, under the guidance of its founder, Ann Lee. "Mother Ann," venerated by her followers, had led them there away from persecutions in Manchester, England. It had been revealed to her, she preached, that God possessed "two natures, the masculine, the feminine, each distinct in function yet one in Being, co-equals in Deity," (Father-Mother God). Hence, equal rights and duties were prescribed for men and women, and the group lived "pure and undefiled," that is, completely celibate. The first organized community of the Shakers was founded on the slopes of Mount

THE SHAKERS AND MEDICINAL HERBS

First U. S. industry in medicinal herbs was carried on by the United Society of Believers in Christ's Second Appearing, commonly known as the Shakers. Begun about 1820, and commercially important by 1830, the medicinal herb industry flourished, hit its peak in the 1860's, then waned at the close of the century. The Shakers gathered or cultivated some 200 varieties; dried, chopped, and pressed them into "bricks"; wrapped, labeled, and sold them to pharmacists and physicians the world over. Tons of solid and fluid extracts also were produced. The Shaker label was recognized for reliability and quality for more than a century.

Lebanon, New York. In general organization, New Lebanon furnished the pattern for all other Shaker societies, and was the spiritual center of the sect.

The medicinal herb industry was a natural outgrowth of the Shakers' early interest in gardening and agriculture, necessary to the self-sufficiency of their communities. The Shakers had entered into the seed business in 1794. The herb business is reported to have been started about 1800, "being the oldest of the kind in the country." According to the *Manifesto* (the official monthly publication of the Society), however, the Shakers did not begin to prepare herbs and roots for sale "for the supply and convenience of apothecaries and druggists" until about 1820. By 1830, herb catalogs were being issued, and shipments were made to London and Paris. By 1831, "about 4,000 pounds of roots and herbs were sent to the market." By 1836, it reached 6,000 pounds; by 1849, 16,500 pounds; by 1852, 42,000 pounds of roots, herbs and barks were pressed, and 7,500 pounds of extracts produced. By 1864, 16,450 pounds of extracts alone were produced.

The Shaker herb industry received its first stimulus about 1820, when "Drs. E. Harlow and G. K. Lawrence, of our society, the latter an excellent botanist, gave their attention to the business, and induced a more systematic arrangement and scientific manner of conducting it, especially as to the seasons for collection, varieties, and methods of preparation." In the early years, wild herbs constituted the main sources of supply; later, cultivation stabilized supplies and qualities. Increasing demand made it necessary, still later, to rely partially on outside growers.

Growth of the Shaker herb industry indicates the reliability which pharmacists and physicians learned to expect of the Shaker labels. The "physics gardens" at New Lebanon by 1850 occupied about 50 acres, given over chiefly to cultivation of hyoscyamus, belladonna, taraxacum, aconite, poppy, lettuce, sage, summer savory, marjoram, dock, burdock, valerian, and horehound. Extract of taraxacum was an important product. About 50 minor plants were also raised. "Nearly 200 varieties of indigenous plants were collected, and 30 or 40 varieties were brought from the South and West and from Europe." Norwood's Tincture of Veratrum Viride, introduced by the Shakers in 1858, became an outstanding specialty that held favor for some eighty years. The Shakers were first to adopt the compressed, or "brick," type of package—small cakes weighing either one ounce or one pound, wrapped in strong paper, and labeled.

The following description of Shaker facilities on the side of Mount Lebanon, based on an interview in 1852, was recorded by Edward Fowler in *The American Journal of Pharmacy:*

"The drying and storing of so many plants requires much space, and several buildings are occupied wholly or in part for this purpose; the principal and central one of which is a neat structure about 120 feet long by 38 feet wide, two stories high with a well-lighted basement and airy garret. The basement is devoted to the pressing, grinding and other heavy work, whilst at one end the steam boiler is placed. The first story is used for packing, papering, sorting, printing and storing the products, whilst the second story and loft are used exclusively for drying and storing. Being well-lighted and airy, these rooms are well fitted for the purpose. Racks of hurdles are conveniently placed along the center on which the herbs previously garbled are put to dry, which is rapidly accomplished by the free circulation of air that is maintained throughout. The sides of the second story room are arranged with large and tight bins, in which the plants are put as soon as they are properly desiccated, until removed for pressing."

The Shakers prepared and packaged pressed herbs in the early 1830's in the herb house of the Church family at New Lebanon. Dried herbs were brought in, chopped by hand, then compressed by hand spiking great wooden screws to force the press into the wooden forms below. The resultant "bricks" then were neatly wrapped on long tables, labeled, and packed in pound units by the sisters. Plain, "Shaker-blue" walls, peg-board molding, handmade equipment, and simple garb, were typically Shaker.

New Lebanon's herb industry received an impetus in 1850 by the addition of such machinery as a steam boiler and a globular-shaped copper vacuum pan for drying extracts. Three power presses, capable of pressing 100 pounds of herbs daily, supplanted the manually operated type.

An interesting sidelight on the herb business at about the time of the Civil War may be found in the writings of Sister Marcia Bullard:

"Forty years ago it was contrary to the orders which governed our lives to cultivate useless flowers, but, fortunately for those of us who loved them, there are many plants which are beautiful as well as useful. We always had extensive poppy beds and early in the morning, before the sun had risen, the white-capped sisters could be seen stooping among the scarlet blossoms to slit those pods from which the petals had just fallen. Again after sundown they came out with little knives to scrape off the dried juice. This crude opium was sold at a large price and its production was one of the most lucrative as well as the most picturesque of our industries.

"The rose bushes were planted along the sides of the road which ran through our village and were greatly admired by the passersby, but it was strongly impressed upon us that a rose was useful, not ornamental. It was not intended to please us by its color or its odor, its mission was to be made into rosewater, and if we thought of it in any other way we were making an idol of it and thereby imperiling our souls. In order that we might not be tempted to fasten a rose upon our dress or to put it into water to keep, the rule was that the flower should be plucked with no stem at all. We had only crimson roses, as they were supposed to make stronger rosewater than the paler varieties. This rosewater was sold, of course, and was used in the community to flavor apple pies. It was also kept in store at the infirmary, and although in those days no sick person was allowed to have a fresh flower to cheer him, he was welcome to a liberal supply of rosewater with which to bathe his aching head."

Rosewater also was used as an eye wash.

While the Church family was chiefly responsible for the Shakers' herb industry, the Second family at New Lebanon, as well as Shaker communities at Watervliet, New York; Harvard, Massachusetts; Canterbury, and Enfield, New Hampshire; New Gloucester, Maine; Groveland, New York; and Union Village, Ohio, contributed importantly to it.

The Shakers' herb business waned with the century, although it is reported that as late as 1890, the services of six brethren and about as many sisters were required. Extracts such as mandrake and colocynth were made until 1900, and Norwood's Tincture of Veratrum Viride survived for at least another four decades.

With no natural progeny to reproduce themselves (the celibate Shakers relied on evangelism, recruitment, and care of orphans, as sources of new members), the Believers' societies began to decline. Some communities had ceased operations before 1900; Watervliet, (formerly Niskeyuna, the first stronghold), terminated in 1938; New Lebanon closed its door in 1947.

By 1956, only some 50 Believers remained in three operating communities—Hancock, Massachusetts; Canterbury, New Hampshire; and New Gloucester, Maine. But the Shaker spirit was still strong within them; and they had reason to be proud of the services their Society rendered, both spiritual and practical, to Pharmacy, Medicine, and to "the outside world" through a dozen other industries and activities.

FOUNDING OF THE AMERICAN PHARMACEUTICAL ASSOCIATION

THE THREE DECADES that followed the founding of North America's first pharmaceutical organization, The Philadelphia College of Pharmacy, in 1821, saw several other such groups spring up. During the same period, there was founded the Pharmaceutical Society of Great Britain (1841), and The American Medical Association (1847). The ground was fallow for nurturing a national pharmaceutical organization. There was needed only the stimulation necessary to plant the seed.

That stimulation was to arise from the necessity for concerted pharmaceutical action against the import of adulterated drugs. The New York College of Pharmacy issued a call to the other Colleges (associations) of Pharmacy in the United States, requesting them to send delegates to a meeting in New York, October 15, 1851, "to take into consideration the subject of standards for the guidance of the Special Examiner of Drugs, Medicines, etc., at the several ports of entry." That convention met in accordance with the call, and, after attending to the matters for which it specially convened, passed resolutions calling for a convention, "consisting of three delegates each, from incorporated and unincorporated pharmaceutical societies, to meet at Philadelphia on the first Wednesday in October, 1852, when all important questions bearing on the profession may be considered, and measures adopted for the organization of a National Association . . ."

The Philadelphia College of Pharmacy made available its Hall on Zane Street to the delegates, and a committee, of which William Procter, Jr., was chairman, proceeded with arrangements. The convention was formally convened at 4 P.M., October 6, 1852,

THE AMERICAN PHARMACEUTICAL ASSOCIATION

Need for better intercommunication among pharmacists; educational and apprentice-ship standards; and quality control of imported drugs, led to calling of a convention of representative pharmacists in the Hall of the Philadelphia College of Pharmacy, October 6 to 8, 1852. Under leadership of its first President, Daniel B. Smith, and first Secretary, William Procter, Jr., the 20 delegates launched The American Pharmaceutical Association; mapped its objectives; and opened its membership to "All pharmaceutists and druggists" of good character who subscribed to its Constitution and Code of Ethics. The Association continues to serve Pharmacy today.

119

with 14 accredited delegates, representing the Colleges of Pharmacy of Massachusetts, Maryland, the City of New York, Richmond, Cincinnati, Philadelphia, plus unincorporated groups in Connecticut.

The delegates were: Daniel B. Smith, Charles Ellis, William

Founders of
The American Pharmaceutical Association

There were 20 pharmacists who took an active part in the founding of The American Pharmaceutical Association. This sketch will serve to identify them in the picture.

1. Daniel B. Smith
   (First President)
2. William Procter, Jr.
   (Corresponding Secretary)
3. George D. Coggeshall
   (Recording Secretary)
4. J. B. H. Campbell
5. Samuel R. Philbrick
6. Samuel M. Colcord
   (Vice President)
7. Edward Parrish
8. Charles Augustus Smith
   (Vice President)
9. John Meakin
10. Alexander Duval
11. Joseph Burnett
12. Llewellyn S. Haskell
13. Charles A. Heinitsh
14. Charles Ellis
15. Henry F. Fish
16. Eugene Dupuy
17. Alfred B. Taylor
   (Treasurer)
18. David Stewart
19. Joseph Laidley
20. Charles L. Bache

They are gathered about the table on the occasion of the signing of the first Code of Ethics of The American Pharmaceutical Association.

Procter, Jr., Joseph Burnett, Samuel M. Colcord, Samuel R. Philbrick, Alexander Duval, Joseph Laidley, David Stewart, Charles Augustus Smith, George D. Coggeshall, Llewellyn S. Haskell, John Meakin, and Henry F. Fish. Four additional gentlemen were invited to seats in the convention: Charles L. Bache, San Francisco, California; Eugene Dupuy, New York; Edward Parrish, and Alfred B. Taylor, of Philadelphia. Two more delegates were accredited the following day: J. B. H. Campbell, Cumberland, Maryland; and Charles A. Heinitsh, Lancaster, Pennsylvania.

First order of business was nomination and election of officers. Daniel B. Smith was named president (he was one of the original organizers of, and had been president of, The Philadelphia College of Pharmacy continuously since 1829; and was to hold the position another two years). Vice presidents were George W. Andrews, Baltimore; Samuel L. Colcord, Boston; and C. Augustus Smith, Cincinnati. Recording secretary was George D. Coggeshall, New York; and corresponding secretary, William Procter, Jr., of Philadelphia (Professor of Pharmacy on the College faculty since 1846, and in later years to be called the Father of American Pharmacy).

A committee appointed the preceding year, chairmaned by Procter, then reported, recommending nine points for the consideration of the Convention:

1. The institution of a National Association, representative in character; formation of a constitution; and preparation of a Code of Ethics for the profession.

2. Encouragement of pharmaceutical education through organization and support of schools of Pharmacy.

3. More attention to the selection and training of apprentices.

4. Investigation of the subjects of secret medicines and quackery.

5. Strengthening of Federal laws, and enactment of State laws to curb traffic in inferior and adulterated drugs.

6. General adoption of the national Pharmacopoeia as a guide in the preparation of officinal medicines.

7. Curbing of indiscriminate sales of poisons.

8. Separation of Pharmacy from the practice of Medicine; discouragement

of physicians from operating pharmacies, and of apothecaries from practicing medicine.

9. Devotion of a part of the Association's programs to, and encouragement of its members to contribute original papers on the sciences, on researches, and on subjects requiring investigation by committees.

Another committee, also headed by Procter, was appointed to study these recommendations and present its proposals to the Convention.

The second day of the Convention, the body adopted a Constitution, the first section of which declared that the proposed national society should be called The American Pharmaceutical Association. Only controversial section was No. 2, setting forth qualifications for membership. "An animated debate ensued" as to whether the organization should be constituted of representative delegate members, or individual members. It is to the credit of this score of foresighted pharmacists that this first constitution finally provided that: "All pharmaceutists and druggists who shall have obtained the age of twenty-one years, whose character, morally and professionally, is fair, and who, after duly considering the obligations of the Constitution and Code of Ethics of this Association are willing to subscribe to them, shall be eligible for membership."

The Convention then proceeded to consider and adopt a Code of Ethics. This Code, which was preceded by the one issued in 1848 by and for The Philadelphia College of Pharmacy, made ably known what the leading American pharmacists of this day considered to be the specific moral obligations of the members of the profession.

Discussion of current problems, especially concerning quality control of imported drugs, followed, with the adoption of a number of resolutions and appointment of committees to further their

122

objectives. Alfred B. Taylor was elected treasurer, and an Executive Committee, consisting of Procter, Coggeshall, and Burnett, was named.

At the final session of the Convention, October 8, the preamble of the Constitution was adopted, thus completing this document, and officially launching the new national organization. The members of the Convention gathered about the table and affixed their names to the new Association's Constitution and Code of Ethics. That these men were far ahead of their time becomes obvious from the fact that in 1857 the recognition of the Code ceased to be one of the presuppositions for membership in the A.Ph.A. It was not until 1922 that, at the instigation of Charles LaWall of The Philadelphia College of Pharmacy and Science, a Code of Ethics was once again adopted by the A.Ph.A.

The American Pharmaceutical Association frequently is referred to as the "mother association" of many of American Pharmacy's specialized organizations—national, regional, state, and local. For example, the largest and lustiest of her children is The National Association of Retail Druggists (whose membership is limited to retail drug store owners or managers), spawned within the A.Ph.A.'s section on Commercial Interests, and born therefrom as a separate association in 1898, with the consent and blessing of the A.Ph.A.

Perhaps the record of The American Pharmaceutical Association during its first century is nowhere better summed up than in an address by Dr. Hugh C. Muldoon, then Dean of Duquesne University School of Pharmacy, and a former president of the A.Ph.A., at the time the Remington Medal was bestowed upon him in 1953:

"This admired and respected association, together with other societies that subscribe to its ideals, form one of pharmacy's superlative strengths.

"Active, vigorous, expanding, the A.Ph.A. is an organization of which all pharmacists can boast. For over a century, it has consistently advanced the prestige of pharmacy and extended its usefulness, arousing, encouraging and informing not only its own members, but all other pharmacists who would listen. Unselfishly, it mothered members of other national, regional, and state associations. More than half the students enrolled in our colleges today are members of its student branches.

"The A.Ph.A. sets standards of professional conduct and excellence. It represents pharmacy's collective conscience. It gave us our exemplary code of ethics. It deals with members by the thousands, but it is happy to serve personally even the most remote and inconspicuous individual pharmacist. Inclusive, rather than exclusive, the Association welcomes to its ranks all who have a legitimate interest in pharmacy. Under expert leadership its thousands of members pool their wisdoms and experiences and hopes and ideals to determine the Association's policies . . ."

WORLD EVENTS AND PHARMACY HISTORY

Dates, persons, and events of significance to the evolution of Pharmacy include:

1888   Institut Pasteur founded.

1888   Roux and Yersin isolated toxin of diphtheria.

1888   Chantemesse and Widal introduced vaccines against typhoid fever.

1888   Celli demonstrated fly transmission of typhoid fever.

1889   Johns Hopkins Hospital (Baltimore) and Hamburg-Eppendorf Hospital opened.

1889   Von Mering and Minkowski produced experimental pancreatic diabetes.

1889   Ramón y Cajal (Spain) demonstrated neurohistological studies at German meeting.

1889   Behring discovered antitoxins.

1889   Vuillemin coined name, "antibiotic."

1889   Kitasato obtained pure cultures of tetanus bacillus.

1889   Pasteur, Chamberland, and Roux employed attenuated cultures in preventive inoculation.

1889   Roux and Yersin pointed out danger of diphtheria convalescents as carriers.

1890   Koch introduced tuberculin and noted that tuberculous animals resist reinoculation.

1890   Schmidt isolated scopolamine.

1890   Behring treated diphtheria with antitoxin.

1890   Schleich introduced infiltration anesthesia.

1890   Ritsert prepared benzocaine.

1890   Jahns synthesized arecoline.

1890   German Pharmaceutical Society (Berlin) founded.

1890-93   Behring and Kitasato developed antitoxin treatment of diphtheria.

1891   Institute for Infectious Diseases (Berlin) opened under Koch.

1891   Frederick G. Banting born.

1891   Lister Institute for Preventive Medicine (London) opened.

1891   Halsted introduced rubber gloves in operative surgery.

1891   Von Bergmann standardized general aseptic ritual in surgery (Koch, 1881; G. Neuber, 1882-5).

1891   Gabriel Lippmann introduced color photography.

1891   S. M. Copeman introduced glycerinated lymph for smallpox vaccination.

1891   Stanford University (California) founded.

1891   Association of American Medical Colleges (Chicago) founded.

1891-93   S. P. Langley experimented with aëroplanes.

1892   Smith and Kilbourne demonstrated tick transmission of bovine piroplasmosis (Texas fever).

1892   Welch and Nuttall identified gas bacillus (*Bacillus aërogenes*).

1892   Sedgwick emphasized necessity of fly control in prevention of typhoid fever.

1893   The Johns Hopkins University School of Medicine opened.

1893   Jean-Martin Charcot died.

1894   Wellcome Physiological Research Laboratories (London) founded.

1894   Field Museum of Natural History (Chicago) founded.

1895   Röntgen discovered x-rays.

1895   Louis Pasteur died.

1895   Ronald Ross demonstrated development of malarial parasite in mosquito.

1895   First pharmaceutical research laboratory established by Parke-Davis.

1895   Calmette introduced serum against snake venoms.

1895   Marconi introduced wireless telegraphy.

1895   Cameron introduced septic tanks for purifying sewage sludge.

1895   Nobel Prize Foundation established at Stockholm.

1895   Friedrich Wilhelms Institut (Berlin) became Kaiser-Wilhelms Akademie.

1896   Max Gruber discovered bacterial agglutination.

1896   Röntgen demonstrated x-rays to public.

1896   Wright, Pfeiffer, and Kolle vaccinated against typhoid fever.

1896   Widal and Sicard introduced agglutination test for typhoid fever.

1896   Leo Arons (Berlin) invented mercury vapor lamp (elimination of red or orange rays).

1896   Friedrich Bezold devised tuning-fork method of testing and training deaf-mutes.

1896   W. J. Dibden and Schweder invented method for bacteriological purification of sewage.

EUROPEAN AND AMERICAN PHARMACY MEET

OVER THE YEARS, no real discord has existed between the representatives of European and American Pharmacy as far as ethical and scientific aims are concerned. However, when groups representing the Old and New Worlds met for the first time, there was great divergence of opinion on subjects pertaining to the compulsory limitation of pharmacies. Sparking the debate from the New World point of view was William Procter, Jr., leader of the American delegation.

Occasion for expression of this point of view, now a classic document of American Pharmacy, was a debate that took place during the Second International Congress of Pharmacy, held in the Salle des Actes of the School of Pharmacy of Paris, France, August 21 to 24, 1867. The first such International Congress had been held in Brunswick, Germany, in 1865; but the Paris meeting was the first at which American delegates were in attendance. This meeting attained the scope, lustre and importance of real internationality.

The delegation from the United States faced a peculiar situation at this convention. In the words of John M. Maisch, first permanent secretary of The American Pharmaceutical Association, reporting at the A.Ph.A. convention one month after the Paris meeting:

"There were three sub-questions on the subject of the practice of Pharmacy.

"First, 'Shall there be unlimited liberty, as in ordinary mercantile business?' All the delegates voted against this proposition; that is where they agreed.

"Second, 'Shall there be free practice in Pharmacy, with the guarantee of a diploma and personal responsibility under the

EUROPEAN AND AMERICAN PHARMACY MEET

Over the years, no real discord has existed between representatives of European and American Pharmacy as far as ethical and scientific aims are concerned. But when the two groups met for the first time, at the Second International Congress of Pharmacy, in Paris, France, August 21 to 24, 1867, there was a great divergence of opinion on the subject of compulsory limitation of pharmacies. William Procter, Jr., leading the delegates of The American Pharmaceutical Association, told the international body that "Public opinion is in America a forceful agent of reform," and that, in his country, "there is not the slightest obstacle toward a multiplication of drug stores save that of lack of success." His declaration vividly documented the American Way of Pharmacy.

common law?' All Europe voted against and all America in favor of free practice and each one personally responsible.

"Third, 'Shall there be a wise regulation by law to protect the public interest?' Our delegation voted against that. Then came the second part of the question, 'of the propriety of limiting the

Key to the Picture

European and American Pharmacy Meet

1. Andrés, Russia
2. Schleisner, Denmark
3. Mosca, Italy
4. Fluckiger, Switzerland
5. Ticell, Sweden
6. Procter, United States
7. Reickher, Germany
8. Robinet, France
9. Ferrari, Spain
10. Walter, Holland

11. Limousin, France

Other delegates and spectators (mostly **French** pharmacists) were seated on several long benches at the mouth of the U-shaped table.

Sixteen nations were represented by delegations at this Second International Congress of Pharmacy. They were: Austria, Belgium, Denmark, Egypt, France, Northern Germany, Southern Germany, Holland, Hungary, Italy, Prussia, Russia, Spain, Sweden, Switzerland, and the United States. England's delegates did not attend.

Artist Robert Thom, in visiting European countries in 1953, contacted the various national pharmaceutical associations, and was able to secure actual portrait reference material for all of the faces that may be seen in the painting.

indefinite multiplication of Pharmaceutical Shops.' All Europe voted for limitation and our delegation voted against it."

"All Europe" did not in this case include England. "It was regretted," says the report of the delegates of the A.Ph.A., "that none of the delegates appointed by the English were present." There is little doubt that the English pharmacists would have joined their American colleagues in their reproach of compulsory regulation of the business of Pharmacy.

This definite split in views could not help but lead to a climax. This came the next day, August 22, in the form of a declaration read in English by Procter, speaking for the delegation from the United States.

"Public opinion," said Procter, "is in America a forceful agent of reforms and has been the main source of progress in Pharmacy. The graduates of the Colleges of Pharmacy enjoy, by virtue of their diplomas, a reputation which gradually makes itself felt and promises a better future . . .

"Another source of amelioration has been the immigration of pharmacists who came to us from Europe and especially from Germany. Some among them exerted a remarkable influence and have helped in the elevation of Pharmacy . . .

"There is, in fact, not the slightest obstacle toward a multiplication of drug stores save that of lack of success. The number of pharmacists existing in a given place is of little importance to another druggist who thinks himself able to satisfy the public better. He will try, and, if he succeeds, some of those who had been established before him may be forced to retire, at least if not the simultaneous growth of population caused by immigration makes a greater number of pharmacies necessary.

"In this way, competition acts as a means of amelioration. In the eyes of those accustomed to the Old World system, this practice may seem somewhat cruel toward those already in business. It is, however, the only one permitted by present-day American public opinion as to the creation of special privileges and, in a country where so many opportunities are open to everyone to make a living, there are no difficulties in changing a career.

"The Pennsylvania (Procter's home state) legislature will accord a charter to any group of citizens making known its intention to teach Medicine, Pharmacy, or Homeopathy. It will, however, not vote a law forbidding other citizens to practice Medicine under these various names or to advertise any other system of Medicine or Pharmacy, and it will not prevent any person, doctor, pharmacist, or empiric, to adopt whatever title seems good to him. Everybody is subject to the law for bad practice, and the law applies quite as well to the negligence of the surgeon as to the ignorance of the quack.

"In thus giving an idea of the present state of Pharmacy in the United States, I have thoroughly reserved my personal opinion. If asked to express it, I am in favor of a system which allows the practice of Pharmacy only to graduates of regular Pharmacy schools and leaves it definitely to the power of competition and to the peculiarities of the profession to regulate the number of those practicing Pharmacy."

The power of competition still regulates American Pharmacy to a large degree, as it does American life in general. Retail Pharmacy in the United States has gone through many changes and many faces. It swung from staid conservatism to screaming commercialism, and then swung again toward dominance of emphasis on the professional side—but still, the American way prevails; and competition of ideas and abilities determines the number of pharmacies and their locations.

It took about 40 years for Procter's dream of making graduation from a recognized American school of Pharmacy the prerequisite for the practice of the profession. Following up on Secretary Maisch's report, the A.Ph.A., at its 1867 meeting, passed a resolution recognizing "the importance of a judicious, but certain, determined, and, as far as practicable, uniform control of the practice of Pharmacy in the various states . . ."

130

In 1868, Secretary Maisch reported to the convention on "Legislation Regulating the Practice of Pharmacy in the United States." A committee was established to draft a model Pharmacy law. A draft of this model law was presented to the association in 1868. This was circulated to the states, and served as a pattern for the majority of state Pharmacy laws until 1900.

It was not until 1904, however, that the first fruit of Procter's dream ripened. The New York State legislature passed a law requiring college graduation, which became effective in 1905.

WORLD EVENTS AND PHARMACY HISTORY

Dates, persons, and events of significance to the evolution of Pharmacy include:

1896	Casper employed ureteral cystoscopy and catheterization in diagnosis of renal diseases.
1896	University of Lyons founded (July 10).
1896	Stenbeck opened Röntgen Institute at Stockholm.
1897	First physiologically standardized pharmaceutical product, fluidextract of ergot, introduced by Parke-Davis.
1897	Shiga discovered dysentery bacillus.
1897	Eijkman cured beriberi with rice polishings.
1897	Emil Fischer synthesized caffeine, theobromine, xanthine, guanine, and adenine.
1897	Jonnesco performed sympathectomy for glaucoma.
1897	Ogata found plague bacilli in fleas of plague-ridden rats.
1897	Nuttall demonstrated fly-transmission of plague bacilli.
1897	Ehrlich stated side-chain theory of immunity.
1897	E. Van Ermengem discovered *Bacillus botulinus*.
1897	J. V. Laborde introduced artificial respiration.

1897	Horton Smith showed danger of chronic (urinary) typhoid carriers.
1897	Germano showed that dryness is fatal to bacteria.
1897-1902	Cannon investigated movements of stomach and intestines by röntgenoscopy.
1897-1904	Ramón y Cajal published treatise on texture of the nervous system.
1898	P. and M. Curie discovered radium.
1898	Howard Florey born.
1898	Loeffler and Frosch investigated filterable viruses.
1898	Looss demonstrated mechanism of hookworm infection.
1898	Theobald Smith isolated and cultivated bovine tubercle bacilli.
1898	Dreser introduced heroin.
1898	Simonds demonstrated transmission of bubonic plague by fleas.
1898	Tschirch explained chemical mechanism of common purgatives.
1898	Affiliation of Rush Medical College with University of Chicago (January 5).
1898	Cornell University Medical College (New York City) founded.
1898-1908	Zeppelin experimented with dirigible airships.

THE FATHER OF
AMERICAN PHARMACY

RARELY has a titular distinction been as deservedly justified as "The Father of American Pharmacy," when applied to William Procter, Jr. It was said of him that "There was no subject which enlisted his attention so much as the advancement of Pharmacy;" and the work he did in the interest of the profession is almost incredible. As the owner of an apothecary shop he set an example. As an editor he was indefatigable. In organized Pharmacy he was a leader. But essentially he was a teacher, and his scientific curiosity knew no limits. The power of his alert mind overcame physical frailty.

Born May 3, 1817, the ninth and youngest child of Isaac Procter, an English Quaker immigrant, the early death of his father denied William Procter, Jr., a liberal education. In 1831, at the age of 14, he entered the pharmacy of Henry M. Zollickoffer at Sixth and Pine Streets, Philadelphia, as an apprentice.

In 1837, he was graduated from the Philadelphia College of Pharmacy, and three years later was elected a member of that society, beginning a long and illustrious association. His contributions to the *American Journal of Pharmacy*, the nation's first pharmaceutical journal, began appearing shortly thereafter.

In 1841, he accepted the position of secretary of the Committee on Revision of the *United States Pharmacopoeia*, and continued to serve on this committee in various capacities for 30 years.

May 12, 1844, he severed his long connection with Apothecary Zollickoffer, and opened his own pharmacy at Ninth and Lombards —a dubious site that he made pay off well.

In 1846, the Philadelphia College of Pharmacy took an important step. It divided the chair of Materia Medica and Pharmacy (existent since 1821) into two—one chair on Materia Medica, and the other on Pharmacy. Procter was unanimously elected the

THE FATHER OF AMERICAN PHARMACY

Rarely has a titular distinction been so deserved. William Procter, Jr., graduated from The *Philadelphia College of Pharmacy in 1837; operated a retail pharmacy; served the College as Professor of Pharmacy for 20 years; was a leader in founding* The American Pharmaceutical Association; *served that organization as its first secretary; later, as its president; served 30 years on the U.S.P. Revision Committee; was for 22 years Editor of the* American Journal of Pharmacy. *In 1869, though retired, Procter continued to edit the Journal in a small publication office located beside the College's Tenth Street building. From retirement he returned to P.C.P.'s chair of Pharmacy in 1872; literally died "in the harness," in 1874.*

Professor of Pharmacy. The high character of his lectures brought him instant fame and appreciation. He held the chair of Pharmacy at P.C.P. continuously from 1846 to 1866.

As a professor and lecturer, Procter soon proved outstanding. No trouble was too great to keep him from bringing to his classes demonstrations to emphasize his points. Pharmacy no longer was a dull, monotonous, mechanical procedure; under Procter's tutelage, it became an art, challenging the best in its practitioners. During these two decades, he continued to operate his pharmacy, to keep up his editorial duties, and to carry on considerable original research, which he published for the benefit of his fellow pharmacists.

"The American Pharmaceutical Association was the offspring of Procter's able and versatile mind," says Albert E. Ebert. His activities in connection with the founding of the A.Ph.A. have previously been recorded. Procter was corresponding secretary of the Association from 1852 to 1857, and a member of its first Executive Committee; first vice president in 1859-1860; and was elected president at its session in Philadelphia in 1862. "Throughout the years of his life that followed the organization," says Ebert, "he gave to it the richest treasures of an intellect fitted beyond all others for the work he had undertaken . . . favorite child of his genius was the American Pharmaceutical Association."

He found time to serve the Philadelphia College of Pharmacy as corresponding secretary from 1855 to 1867; second vice president, 1868-1869; and first vice president, 1869-1874.

Among Procter's many investigations in the field of phytochemistry, his experiments with *Betula lenta* (birch) and *Gaultheria procumbens* (wintergreen) attracted much attention. They proved the volatile oil gained from the one as well as the other to be the same, "a hydracid analogous to saliculous acid." One can imagine how pleased Procter was when the renowned French chemist, Cahours, recognized this "hydracid" as methyl salicylate.

Another of his contributions to Pharmacy was the editing and enlarging of Mohr and Redwood's *Practical Pharmacy*, which Procter offered to American readers in 1849 as the first text of its kind published in the United States.

Many years of close attention to his varied and demanding duties necessitated a change for this man who was never physically strong. In 1866, he resigned his chair of Pharmacy. In 1867, he determined to take a trip to Europe—a "postman's holiday," indeed, for he found time on this trip to serve as delegate from the American Pharmaceutical Association to the International Pharmaceutical Congress held that year in Paris.

Procter's career as an editor was no less illustrious than his many other activities. He began contributing articles in 1840, soon after his election to membership in the College. In 1846, in addition to operating his pharmacy and beginning his teaching duties, Procter became associated with Professor Joseph Carson as coeditor of the *American Journal of Pharmacy*. Upon Carson's retirement in 1850, Procter assumed sole editorial charge.

This, the first pharmaceutical journal published in the United States, began as a slim pamphlet entitled *The Journal of the Philadelphia College of Pharmacy* in 1825, only four issues of which appeared in the first four years, under the editorship of Samuel Jackson. In 1829, Dr. Benjamin Ellis became its editor; in 1831, Dr. R. Eglesfield Griffith took over until 1835, when the name was changed to the *American Journal of Pharmacy*.

Procter "filled the pages of this journal with valuable material adapted to the needs and contributing to the education of American pharmacists." In the 22 volumes of the magazine for which he was responsible, there are 550 original articles bearing his by-line, apart from numerous editorials and extracts. After he retired from his first professorship, Procter divided his time between his pharmacy and his editorial work, which was carried on in the *Journal's* small office beside Philadelphia College of Pharmacy's Tenth Street building.

The depth of Procter's devotion to the editorial side of his career may be gauged from this editorial in the *Journal* of April 1, 1871: "The Retiring Editor to his Friends and Readers:"

"The path editorial has not always been found smooth and free from thorns; not a few instances have occurred where the line of duty has run very nearly athwart that of personal friendship, causing a feeling of soreness. At other times offence has unintentionally been given; yet as the governing motive has been based on a sense of rectitude, he has continued his course steadily onward, accepting the result. So far as is remembered, most of the wounds thus occasioned have kindly healed . . . In returning among his fellow-pharmacists, the Editor disclaims the idea of ceasing to be a worker, and it is not improbable that he may occasionally claim a few pages as a volunteer, and in other ways continue to aid the cause of pharmacy."

He relinquished the editorial reins after having seen the *Journal* become a monthly publication.

But for the worker, there is always a task. In 1872, the College's chair of Pharmacy became vacant, due to the death of Professor Edward Parrish. The Trustees turned instinctively to William Procter, Jr. After some consideration, Procter replied that, "whilst adhering to the opinion previously given, that a younger and more energetic man would have been better for the ultimate advantage of the School, I acquiesce in the present necessity for a teacher with some experience, and accept the appointment, promising my best efforts under the short notice received."

The end of Procter's career came in a way that probably would have been his choice—in the harness. The lectures of 1873-74 had progressed as far as February 9. On that evening he delivered his usual lecture, was pleased with the attention accorded him, and returned home in apparent usual health. Shortly after falling asleep, a disturbance in respiration aroused the family, but before medical assistance could be called, his life had ceased.

NOTE: William Procter, Jr., is prominent in three consecutive pictures in this series ("Founding of the American Pharmaceutical Association," "European and American Pharmacy Meet," and "The Father of American Pharmacy"). It will be noted that his appearance changes with age. Prior to his European tour, in 1867, Procter "kept his face cleanly shaved; but while absent he allowed his whiskers and moustache to grow, and continued that custom for the remainder of his life." (*Memoir*, 1874.)

136

WORLD EVENTS AND PHARMACY HISTORY

Dates, persons, and events of significance to the evolution of Pharmacy include:

1899	Reed, Carroll, Lazear, and Agramonte demonstrated mosquito transmission of yellow fever.
1899	Charles Best born.
1899	Ramón y Cajal described histology of cerebral cortex.
1899	Weichselbaum and Jaeger isolated meningococcus.
1899	Grassi and Bignami proved that *Anopheles* is sole transmitter of malaria.
1899	H. Dreser introduced aspirin.
1899	Dewar liquefied air, oxygen, and hydrogen.
1899	Beijerinck isolated filterable virus of mosaic tobacco disease.
1899	Medical Library Association (United States) founded.
1899	Ehrlich's Institute for Experimental Medicine (Frankfurt) founded.
1899-1900	Reed completed demonstration of mosquito transmission of yellow fever.
1899-1900	Stenbeck treated cancer with Röntgen rays.
1900	Bier introduced spinal (cocaine) anesthesia into general surgery.
1900	Wertheim devised radical operation for uterine cancer.
1900	A. Walkhoff showed destructive effect of radium on the tissues.
1900	Willstätter and Bode produced synthetic cocaine.
1900	Park recommended control of milk (New York City) by bacterial tests.
1900	Woodhead disinfected water supply of Maidstone (England) with chlorine after typhoid epidemic.
1900	College of Physicians and Surgeons (Chicago) became College of Medicine, University of Illinois (May 1).
1900	Conference of Pharmaceutical Faculties founded. (Became American Association of Colleges of Pharmacy in 1925.)
1900-1903	Leishman and Donovan discovered protozoön of kala azar.
1901	De Vries stated mutation theory.
1901	Dutton and Ford discovered trypanosome of sleeping sickness (*Trypanosoma gambiense*).
1901	Aschkinazi and Caspari showed that radium checked the growth of bacteria.
1901	Landsteiner discovered blood-grouping (iso-agglutination).
1901	Emil Fischer devised ester method of isolating amino acids.
1901	Takamine isolated Adrenalin.
1901	Rockefeller Institute for Medical Research (New York) opened.
1901	German Society for History of Medicine and Science (Leipzig) founded.
1901	Award of Nobel prizes begun. First recipients included Röntgen and von Behring for their contributions on x-rays and on serum therapy for diphtheria.
1902	Carrel introduced new methods of vascular anastomosis and transplantation of tissues.
1902	Walter Reed died.
1902	Bayliss and Starling discovered secretin.
1902	R. Herzog discovered site of Asclepieion at Cos.
1902	Holzknecht devised method of dosimetry for x-rays.
1902	P. C. Hewitt perfected quartz mercury vapor lamp.
1902	McClung isolated sex chromosome.
1902	Ravenel isolated bovine tubercle bacillus from a tuberculous child.
1902	Schild introduced atoxyl.
1902	Steinbuchel introduced morphine-scopolamine anesthesia in obstetrics.
1902	Finney performed gastroduodenostomy.
1902	Carnegie Institution of Washington founded.
1902	Société Française d'Histoire de Médecine (Paris) founded.
1902	Nobel prize awarded to Ronald Ross for advancing knowledge on malaria.
1902-1903	Jensen propagated cancer through several generations of mice.
1902-1906	Bayliss and Starling investigated hormones.

A REVOLUTION IN PHARMACEUTICAL EDUCATION

THE PATH OF PROGRESS frequently is impeded by the stubborn thorns of resistance to change. Progress in pharmaceutical education in the United States had to travel this thorny path.

Enjoying only a hesitant growth before the Civil War, pharmaceutical education, like all education, suffered in its aftermath. The independent association school, of which The Philadelphia College of Pharmacy was the most distinguished model, exemplified the dominant pattern of pharmaceutical education of the period.

There seems to be some doubt about which college or university (as differentiated from independent pharmacy schools supported by associations of pharmacists), was first to offer pharmaceutical courses on a collegiate level. A laboratory course in Pharmacy was offered in 1860 by Professor Silas H. Douglas at the University of Michigan, but its main purpose was to instruct medical students. It was not until eight years later, in 1868, that a full course of study in Pharmacy was offered at the University of Michigan, although as early as 1839 the Regents had charged the professor of geology and mineralogy "with the subjects of Chemistry and Pharmacy."

Baldwin University (a small private institution in Berea, Ohio) appears in 1865 to have become the first place where pharmacy instruction began as part of a general college program. The first state-supported institution known to have graduated a few men in Pharmacy was the Medical College of the State of South Carolina in 1867.

It was the course in Pharmacy launched in 1868 at the University of Michigan, which became a separate School of Pharmacy in 1876, and the kindly, scholarly, but determined professor in whose hands the direction of the course, and later the school, were entrusted, that were to have a most far-reaching effect upon phar-

A REVOLUTION IN PHARMACEUTICAL EDUCATION

When Dr. Albert B. Prescott launched the pharmacy course at the University of Michigan in 1868, critical attention was aroused because he abandoned the traditional requirement of pregraduation apprenticeship. At the 1871 convention of the American Pharmaceutical Association, he was denied credentials and virtually ostracized. However, the Michigan course pioneered several other major changes: laboratory pharmacy, a definite curriculum that included basic sciences, and a program that demanded students' full-time attention. During the next 30 years, Dr. Prescott had the satisfaction of seeing his once revolutionary innovations generally adopted by pharmaceutical faculties.

139

maceutical education. A revolution was beginning to take place—one that would require more than three decades to evolve from radical innovation to accepted practice. The man who sparked this revolution was Dr. Albert Benjamin Prescott.

Most startling (to contemporary educators) of the innovations at the University of Michigan was the complete disregard of apprenticeship as a requirement for graduation as a pharmacist. This "practical" experience had been the very foundation of education in the independent Pharmacy schools—experience that was "rounded off" and systematized by lecture courses usually held at night after a day's work in the store. Independent schools clung to this tradition, and other university schools only reluctantly followed the lead of the University of Michigan in omitting apprenticeship altogether. Dr. Prescott stubbornly held his ground, defending his course, not through any lack of appreciation of the value of actual experience, but because he felt that the way the requirement was enforced was a farce.

While attention focused on the University of Michigan largely because of this flouting of the tradition of pregraduation apprenticeship, the Michigan course foreshadowed and pioneered several other major changes in American pharmaceutical education—notably, laboratory work and instruction, and a definite curriculum which included the sciences basic to Pharmacy, and which demanded nearly the full-time attention of the student.

Dr. Prescott's revolutionary ideas and practices clashed head on with pharmaceutical educators and organizations of the day, when he arrived at the convention of the American Pharmaceutical Association held in St. Louis in 1871. When the session opened on September 12, a hot debate ensued. The delegates seemed to sense that Dr. Prescott's presence symbolized a challenge to the current status of pharmaceutical teaching. It was decided to admit the 39-year-old Dr. Prescott as a member, but to deny him a seat as a delegate, holding that within the meaning of the Constitution and By-laws, the University of Michigan was not "a College of Pharmacy, it being neither an organization controlled by pharmacists, nor an institution of learning which, by its rules and requirements, insures to its graduates the proper practical training . . .''

Dr. Prescott obtained the floor the following day, and delivered a memorable address. It was forthright and fair. He championed scientific education in Pharmacy, and decried emphasis on an apprenticeship which, in the majority of instances, had to be under a preceptor who "has little more science than his apprentice"; who himself "also was a blind apprentice, if he was an apprentice at all"; and who "is too often unconscious or regardless of his own deficiencies . . .''

"It is the growing conviction of thoughtful educators," Prescott continued, "that physical science must be, and is to be taught in college laboratories. The student must handle the materials and wield the forces of physical and chemical action before he obtains a clear acquaintance with the same. And it is more than knowledge of natural forces, it is the skill to guide those forces that constitutes power, and such skill is best acquired in school laboratories . . .''

For a long time, Dr. Prescott and the University of Michigan stood alone; but Dr. Prescott had the satisfaction of seeing his ideas eventually adopted by all schools and colleges of Pharmacy. Furthermore, 28 years later, he had the honor of serving as president of The American Pharmaceutical Association (1899-1900) which in 1871 had virtually ostracized him. The following year (1900-1901), he was an organizer and first president of the Conference of Pharmaceutical Faculties (now the American Association of Colleges of Pharmacy).

Albert B. Prescott was born December 12, 1832, in Hastings, New York, in the ninth generation from John Prescott, who came to Boston from England in 1640. Albert's grandfather, Col. William Prescott, was commander of the colonial troops at the Battle of Bunker Hill.

At the age of nine, Albert Prescott injured his right knee in a fall, resulting in a crooked leg, and forcing him to use a cane the rest of his life. He entered the Department of Medicine and Surgery at the University of Michigan in 1860, graduating in 1864 and entering the Medical Service of the United States Army.

Upon his discharge in 1865, Dr. Prescott returned to the University of Michigan as assistant professor of Chemistry. When the course in Pharmacy began in 1868, Dr. Prescott was charged with its administration. Eight years later, in 1876, the course was organized as a separate School of Pharmacy. Dr. Prescott guided the school for the next three decades.

In addition to the honors eventually bestowed upon him by Pharmacy, Dr. Prescott had many from other fields in which he was interested. He became a Fellow of the Chemical Society of London in 1886; was one of the organizers and president of the American Chemical Society in 1886; he was president of the American Association for the Advancement of Science in 1891; he was granted an honorary membership in the Philadelphia College of Pharmacy in 1892; his own university conferred the degree of Doctor of Philosophy on him in 1886, and Doctor of Laws in 1896; and Northwestern University conferred an LL.D. on him in 1902.

Dr. Prescott has been described as "one of the most modest of men—a remarkable combination of gentleness and strength, in which gentleness held the balance of power . . . a man of wide sympathies and far-reaching interests." Michigan's Dean-Emeritus Edward W. Kraus, who knew Dr. Prescott personally and who was one of those to succeed him as head of the College of Pharmacy, described Prescott as "one of the great leaders of the country in Pharmacy and Chemistry . . . a man greatly interested in students." Dr. Henry Vaughan, Dean of the School of Public Health, stated publicly that "Dr. Prescott's work gave rise to the country's first laboratory for public health work," and that "much of what we have in public health today came out of the laboratories of Dr. Prescott." Dr. Prescott remained active in his several fields of endeavor until his death, February 25, 1905.

Thus came about a revolution in pharmaceutical education, led by a kind and gentle professor with a large and exact knowledge, combined with a capacity and a disposition to impart it to others. Pharmacy has benefited immeasurably from his endeavors.

WORLD EVENTS AND PHARMACY HISTORY

Dates, persons, and events of significance to the evolution of Pharmacy include:

1903   License No. 1 "for the manufacture of viruses, serums, toxins, and analogous products," issued by U. S. Treasury Dept. to Parke-Davis.

1903   Metchnikoff inoculated higher apes with syphilis.

1903   Einthoven developed the electrocardiograph.

1903   Von Pirquet and Schick identified serum sickness with anaphylaxis.

1903   Koch stressed danger of healthy typhoid carriers as agents of infection.

1903   Emil Fischer and von Mehring introduced veronal (barbital).

1903   Albers-Schönberg noted sterilizing effect of x-rays on gonads.

1903   Bruce demonstrated transmission of sleeping sickness by tsetse fly.

1903   Dunbar discovered toxin and antitoxin (pollantin) of hay fever.

1903   Riva Rocci invented sphygmomanometer.

1903   Ramsay and Soddy demonstrated transmutation of radium into helium.

1903   Siedentopf and Zsigmondy invented ultramicroscope.

1903   Almroth Wright and Douglass investigated opsonins.

1903   Castellani discovered *Trypanosoma ugandense*.

1903   Vaccination obligatory in Spain.

1903   Nobel prize awarded to Becquerel and the Curies for their contributions on radiation.

1904   Nobel prize awarded to Pavlov for his work on physiology of digestion.

1904   Atwater invented respiration calorimeter.

1904-14   Gen. William Crawford Gorgas, U. S., headed yellow fever control making possible building of Panama Canal.

1904   Max Cloetta introduced digalen.

1904   Ehrlich discovered trypan red, effective against trypanosomes.

1904   Fourneau introduced stovaine.

1904   Ramón y Cajal published *Texture of the Nervous System of Man and of the Other Vertebrates*.

1904   F. Stolz determined composition of Adrenalin.

1905   F. R. Schaudinn and Erich Hoffmann discovered parasite of syphilis (*Treponema pallidum*).

1905   Bordet and Gengou isolated bacillus of whooping cough.

1905   Chaput employed stovaine in spinal anesthesia.

1905   Winter resuscitated the heart by Adrenalin injections.

1905   Dutton and Koch demonstrated tick transmission of African relapsing fever.

1905   E. H. Starling, English physiologist, first used the term, "hormone."

1905   Alfred Einhorn discovered novocain.

1905   Wright brothers made successful flight with aëroplane.

1905   Nobel prize awarded to Koch for his work on tuberculosis.

1906   Wassermann introduced serum diagnosis of syphilis.

1906   Ernst B. Chain born.

1906   Frederick G. Hopkins (England) predicted isolation of vitamins.

1906   Von Pirquet stated doctrine of allergy.

1906   Voelcker and von Lichtenberg examined kidney with x-ray (pyelography).

1906   Neisser demonstrated susceptibility of lower apes to syphilis.

1906   Federal Food and Drugs Act (United States) passed (June 30; effective 1907).

1906   Nobel prize awarded to Golgi and Ramón y Cajal for their work on structure of the nervous system.

1906-25   Blair Bell introduced use of pituitrin as oxytocic in lingering labor.

1907   Von Pirquet introduced cutaneous reaction in tuberculosis.

1907   Theobald Smith suggested use of toxin-antitoxin in diphtheria (Behring, 1912).

1907   Ricketts demonstrated tick transmission of Rocky Mountain fever.

1907   Adolf Schmidt employed functional test meal in diagnosing intestinal disorders.

1907   Fletcher and Hopkins demonstrated role of lactic acid formation in normal muscle contraction.

1907   Nobel prize awarded to Alphonse Laveran for discovering the etiology of protozoan diseases.

THE PHARMACOPOEIA
COMES OF AGE

ISSUANCE of the first *United States Pharmacopoeia* in 1820 was a unique forward step in the science and literature of medicine. It was the first book of drug standards, according to the *Medical Repository*, "ever compiled by the authority of the profession throughout a nation . . ."

Following the publication of the first official pharmacopoeia in Florence in 1498, many collections of formulas and compendiums were made in various countries. The Colleges of Great Britain had developed books of this sort; and France, by command of her monarch, had furnished her *Codex*. But it remained for American physicians to frame a work which emanated from the profession itself, founded on the principles of democratic representation, and accepted throughout the nation.

This first edition of the *United States Pharmacopoeia* was definitely the work of the medical profession. There were no pharmaceutical associations whose cooperation could be invited. The physicians responsible for the Philadelphian second edition (1831) asked for and received valuable assistance from members of the Philadelphia College of Pharmacy (the name of the first pharmaceutical association and also the first pharmaceutical educational institution in the United States, organized in 1821, the year after issuance of the first *U.S.P.*). Advice of representatives of pharmaceutical organizations was increasingly sought by each succeeding revision committee.

By 1870, there was no doubt that the pharmaceutical interest in the *U.S.P.* had grown, while the medical interest had decreased. This situation led Dr. Edward R. Squibb, physician, pharmaceutical manufacturer, and teacher, to offer a suggestion for a change in the revision program. Dr. Squibb's proposal asked for

ROBERT THOM

THE PHARMACOPOEIA COMES OF AGE

The first "United States Pharmacopoeia," issued in 1820, was the work of the medical pro-
fession. It was the first book of drug standards from a professional source to have achieved a
nation's acceptance. In 1877, the "U.S.P." was in danger of dissolution due to the lack of
interest of the medical profession. Dr. Edward R. Squibb, manufacturing pharmacist as
well as physician, took the problem to The American Pharmaceutical Association convention.
Pharmacists formed a "Committee on Revision." Under chairmanship of hospital pharma-
cist Charles Rice, assisted by pharmacist-educator Joseph P. Remington, and their inde-
fatigable collaborator, Dr. Squibb, the "U. S. Pharmacopoeia" surged to new importance.

the cooperative action of The American Medical Association (founded in 1847) and The American Pharmaceutical Association (founded in 1852) "under the fully recognized leadership of the former," with the whole management and control to "be entrusted to a sub-organization . . . to be called the Pharmaceutical Council of the American Medical Association."

The plan seemed to find favor with the A.M.A. at its meeting at Philadelphia in 1876. A few months later, members of the A.Ph.A., also meeting in Philadelphia, expressed the opinion that "the medical profession certainly have a right to direct what substances shall enter into the pharmacopoeia, their general character, and their preparations, but the details of the work devolve certainly upon pharmacy and pharmaceutical chemists."

Dr. Squibb presented his plan in detail to The American Medical Association at its meeting in Chicago in 1877—but to his surprise, he met a hostile and almost abusive reception. Three months later, at the 1877 meeting of The American Pharmaceutical Association at Toronto, Ontario, Canada, Dr. Squibb reported that "the American Medical Association has distinctly refused to have anything to do with this subject," and that he was through attempting to be a reformer.

Then the unexpected happened. Frederick Hoffmann, German-born New York pharmacist, author, and journalist, posed the question whether the time had arrived "when this Association, as the foremost exponent of American Pharmacy, and as the proper and competent custodian of the interests and status of both, the profession and the pharmacopoeia, is entitled and is duty bound to indicate its prerogative . . . in both the labor and the management of the pharmacopoeia."

The result was the acceptance of a resolution which asked for the appointment of "a Committee on the Revision of the *United States Pharmacopoeia*, consisting of fifteen members of the American Pharmaceutical Association who shall, by a plan to be determined by themselves, be instructed to prepare the text of the proposed new *Pharmacopoeia* . . ."

When the A.Ph.A. selected Charles Rice, chief pharmacist at Bellevue Hospital in New York, to develop and lead a program for the guidance of the *U.S.P.* Revision Committee, it made a most wise choice. Dr. Rice had not only excellent experience, but excellent facilities for experimentation, and the acquaintance and confidence of leaders both in Pharmacy and Medicine. On December 28, 1877, he called a meeting at the New York College of Pharmacy to discuss his plan for the revision program. Among those present were Professors John M. Maisch and Joseph P. Remington of Philadelphia; Professor G. F. H. Markoe and S. A. D. Sheppard of Boston; Professor P. W. Bedford, Dr. E. R. Squibb and Frederick Hoffmann, New York.

One year later, in 1878, a report of the committee was accepted by The American Pharmaceutical Association at its meeting in Atlanta. It was read by Chairman Rice, who possessed remarkable "energy and wonderful talent of organizing."

This A.Ph.A. committee made its report at the Pharmacopoeial Convention of 1880, and Dr. Rice was elected a member of the Revision Committee and then chosen its chairman. As the work of the committee progressed, other illustrious names are to be found in the record, including Professor A. B. Prescott, C. Lewis Diehl, Charles Mohr, Charles Bullock, Professor Emlen Painter, Professor W. T. Wenzell, Professor John Uri Lloyd, and Professor Oscar Oldberg. Meetings of the full committee were infrequent, due to the distances which separated the members; but Chairman Rice overcame this difficulty by laboriously writing in longhand full circulars of all reports and procedures, duplicating these by a hektograph process, and mailing them to members. A scrapbook of these 11″ x 17″ sheets, permanently bound, makes a book fourteen inches thick, which is still in the possession of the Pharmacopoeial organization at its headquarters building at 46 Park Avenue, New York.

While much of the work of revision was carried on by correspondence, there is evidence that Chairman Rice's library, adjacent to the dispensary at Bellevue Hospital, was the scene of many momentous discussions. Vice Chairman Remington often visited him there, as did **Dr. Squibb**.

When, in 1882, the new edition of the *U. S. Pharmacopoeia* appeared, it was, as has been stated by Urdang, "certainly worth all the trouble . . . American pharmacy had to come to the rescue of the *United States Pharmacopoeia* at a moment of dissolution, and it has continued the job of safeguarding the continuity and adequacy of the work ever since."

Charles Rice

Of a singularly modest disposition, devotion to duty was perhaps Dr. Rice's most strongly marked characteristic. No sacrifice of personal comfort or much needed rest was too great for him to make in doing what he believed to be his duty.

Born in Munich, October 4, 1841, Charles Rice (originally spelled Reis) was educated in that city, in Passau, and in Vienna. He became particularly proficient in languages, reading some sixteen with ease. At one time he was considered one of the world's best Sanskrit scholars. He came to the United States in 1862, entered the U. S. Navy as a hospital steward, serving three years. A severe attack of malarial fever sent him to Bellevue Hospital. Upon convalescence, he became assistant to John Frey, apothecary of the institution; and upon Mr. Frey's death he was appointed superintendent of, and chemist to, the general drug department of the hospital. Later, he became chemist to the Public Charities and Corrections of the City of New York. He held both positions throughout his life.

When the Pharmacopoeial Convention met May 5, 1880, the plan for guidance of the Committee on Revision, which Dr. Rice had prepared at the direction of the A.Ph.A., found such favor that he was elected a member of the Committee on Revision and became its chairman. The *Pharmacopoeia* issued by his committee represented such a marked advance over its predecessors that he was re-elected chairman of the committee in 1890, and again in 1900.

In 1885, Dr. Rice was elected chairman of the Committee on Unofficial Formulas of the body that had published the *New York and Brooklyn Formulary*. The A.Ph.A. in the same year also appointed him chairman of a similar committee. In these capacities, Dr. Rice arranged a plan whereby the *New York and Brooklyn Formulary* was turned over to The American Pharmaceutical Association. This work, immensely enlarged in scope and usefulness, is now the companion book to the *U.S.P.*, and is known as the *National Formulary*.

In the course of his earlier work, Dr. Rice was victim of a laboratory explosion and was severely burned about the face and scalp. To cover scars of this injury

Dr. Rice adopted a peculiar hair configuration that became a well-recognized feature.

Dr. Rice became a member of the College of Pharmacy of the City of New York in 1868; and a trustee in 1870, in which capacity he served until his death, in 1901. As teacher, examiner, chairman of the Library Committee, and curator, he served the College for over thirty years.

Dr. E. R. Squibb

Contemporary with Dr. Rice in his interest in the College of Pharmacy of the City of New York was Dr. Edward Robinson Squibb, who gave his services as a teacher without compensation from 1869 to 1871. Contemporary, too, was their interest in the *United States Pharmacopoeia*.

Dr. Squibb was born in Wilmington, Delaware, July 4, 1819, of Quaker parentage. He served an apprenticeship to a pharmacist in Philadelphia from 1837 to 1842, then entered the Jefferson Medical College in Philadelphia, graduating in 1845 with an M.D. degree. In 1847, he entered the United States Navy. After various tours of duty at sea, he was given a task in the establishment of a pharmaceutical laboratory for the manufacture of medicines for the Navy. Dr. Squibb became assistant director. It was here, probably, that in 1852 ether was first made by steam distillation.

Dr. Squibb resigned his commission in the Navy in 1857. In 1859, Dr. R. S. Satterlee, Chief Medical Purveyor to the U. S. Army, induced Dr. Squibb to secure outside capital and establish a small laboratory of his own in Brooklyn, in part to supply the Army's needs. When this laboratory was scarcely well under way, on the evening of December 24, 1858, the building was completely destroyed by fire resulting from an explosion, and Dr. Squibb was so badly burned he was convalescent for many months and disfigured for life. Following this, he began to grow a full beard. His eyelids were injured, giving him an appearance of staring; and he lost his right hand.

By the middle of 1859, the premises were rebuilt and refurnished, and the business again launched. Later, Dr. Squibb admitted his two sons, Edward H. Squibb, a physician, and Charles F. Squibb, into the business, which has continued since under the name of E. R. Squibb & Sons.

An indefatigable worker, a voluminous writer, a pioneer in research and in the manufacture of pharmaceutical and chemical preparations of high purity, Dr. Squibb took an early interest in the *United States Pharmacopoeia*. He was a delegate from the New York Academy of Medicine to the Pharmacopoeial Convention of 1860, and was elected a member of the Committee on Revision. He continued to take an active and lively interest in the *Pharmacopoeia*, whether in or out of official capacity, throughout his life.

A characteristic of Dr. Squibb was his interest in and encouragement and assistance to young men. His services to the professions of Pharmacy and

Medicine consisted not only of the mass of work he himself accomplished, but also of what he enabled others to do.

Dr. Squibb was a member of The American Medical Association, and joined The American Pharmaceutical Association in 1858; he belonged to the American Chemical Society, and was an honorary member of the Pharmaceutical Society of Great Britain.

Death came to Dr. Squibb on October 25, 1900, as a result of an occlusion of the coronary artery.

Joseph P. Remington

Among the young men whom Dr. E. R. Squibb taught and encouraged was one who was destined to become perhaps American Pharmacy's greatest teacher, and to rank close to his predecessor, William Procter, Jr., as one of Pharmacy's greats. He was Joseph Price Remington.

Born March 26, 1847, Joseph Remington was the son of a Philadelphia physician. On his mother's side he was a descendant of Townsend Speakman, an apothecary in Philadelphia some hundred years before Remington's birth.

Exactly fifty-five years before the day of his death, he entered the establishment of Charles Ellis, Son & Company, as a pharmacy apprentice. At that time, his preceptor, Charles Ellis, was president of the Philadelphia College of Pharmacy. The young man was encouraged to attend the course of lectures, and graduated from the institution in 1866. The following year, Mr. Remington went to Brooklyn to enter the employ of Dr. Squibb. This afforded an unusual opportunity for him to amass a prodigious fund of technical and professional knowledge. During this three-year association, Mr. Remington lived in the home of Dr. Squibb. Therefore, his association with the manufacturer and his friend, Charles Rice, was a very close one.

Mr. Remington returned to Philadelphia, entering the employ of Powers and Weightman. In 1871, he accepted a teaching position with the Philadelphia College of Pharmacy. The following year he established his own retail pharmacy which he continued to operate for thirteen years. At the College, he became assistant to Professor Procter. When Professor Procter passed away in 1874, Mr. Remington was elected to the full professorship in Pharmacy, a position he held for forty-four years.

Professor Remington's affiliation with The American Pharmaceutical Association began in 1868. He served this organization in many outstanding ways: in 1880, by aiding in establishment of the Council as its governing body, and as Council chairman; in 1887, by developing a plan for the Association's reorganization, and establishing the several sections; as delegate to the A.M.A.; and, in 1893, as its president. His first connection with pharmacopoeial revision work was in 1877. He was a member of the United States Pharmacopoeial

Convention in 1880, and there was named first vice president of the Revision Committee. He served in this capacity under Chairman Rice until the latter's death in 1901. At that time, Professor Remington was elected chairman, a position which he held until his death. It was during Professor Remington's chairmanship that the *U.S.P.* received its legal standing under the Federal and State Pure Food and Drugs Acts.

His was a busy life. In addition to the activities mentioned, Dr. Remington became one of the associate editors of the *United States Dispensatory;* and in 1885, his great work, *Remington's Practice of Pharmacy*, was first issued. Succeeding editions of this have probably made it the most widely known textbook in Pharmacy.

In 1893, Dr. Remington was elected dean of the Philadelphia College of Pharmacy—another position which he held until his death, January 1, 1918.

His deep, abiding faith in the nobility and dignity of Pharmacy as a profession probably was Dr. Remington's strongest trait. He has justly been called a teacher of teachers, for many of those who studied under Remington went forth to carry the torch of knowledge to other generations of pharmacists in the colleges of the land.

The *United States Pharmacopoeia*, too, has gone forward from the fateful day in 1877 when American Pharmacy took over its leadership. The names of Rice, Remington and Squibb illumine its path; but many great men of both Pharmacy and Medicine have added their invaluable contributions. In the Revision Committee chair, Dr. E. Fullerton Cook served for three decades; and the great work continued forward under the guidance of Dr. Lloyd Miller, who took over the helm in 1950.

THE STANDARDIZATION
OF PHARMACEUTICALS

DESPITE the professional skill and integrity of nineteenth-century pharmacists, seldom did two preparations of vegetable drugs have the same strength, even though prepared by identical processes. Crude drug plants varied widely in active alkaloidal or glucosidal content, and this variation—reflected in the galenical preparations made from them—caused great concern to the prescribing physician and to the manufacturing pharmacist. Patients for whom such preparations were prescribed might receive the normal, expected benefits; no benefits at all; or, distressing effects due to toxic overstrengths.

That the first significant steps toward the answer to this problem came from the laboratories of Parke, Davis & Company in Detroit, Michigan, seems undisputed. With little fanfare, this thirteen-year-old pharmaceutical house introduced *Liquor Ergotae Purificatus* into its line in September, 1879. This standardization of ergot, then so useful in the control of conditions associated with childbirth, was a great step forward in Pharmacy's service to mankind. Rapidly, there followed a series of other "normal liquids," which actually were standardized fluid extracts.

The story of drug standardization has been well summed up by Dr. George Urdang in a special monograph, from which we quote:

"The *Real-Enzyklopadie der Gesamten Pharmazie*, compiled by Professor Josef Moeller (Vienna) and Professor Hermann Thoms (Berlin), explains in 1908 (Volume 11, page 548) the term 'Standardpraparate' as follows:

"Standardized preparations are such drugs, tinctures and extracts which have been brought to a certain amount of their effective contents. Originally this had been tried, although in a rather unsatisfactory way, in the United States of America and in England,

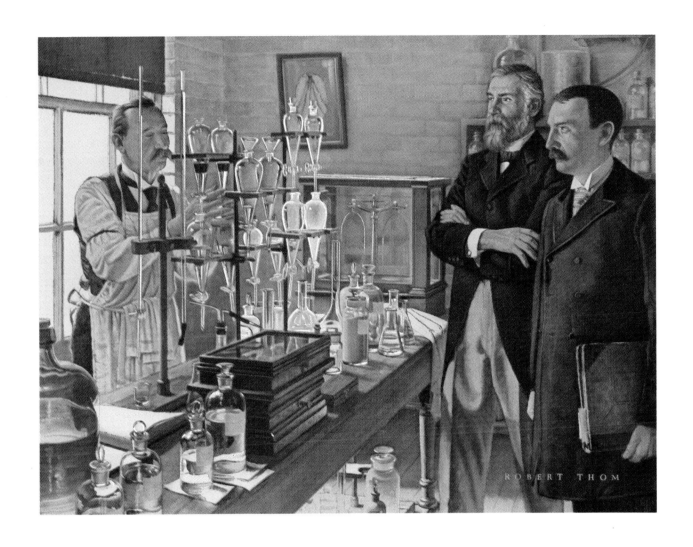

THE STANDARDIZATION OF PHARMACEUTICALS

Despite the professional skill and integrity of 19th-century pharmacists, seldom did two preparations of vegetable drugs have the same strength, even though prepared by identical processes. Crude plant drugs varied widely in active alkaloidal and gluco-sidal content. First answer to this problem came when Parke, Davis & Company introduced standardized "Liquor Ergotae Purificatus" in 1879. Dr. Albert Brown Lyons, as the firm's Chief Chemist, further developed methods of alkaloidal assay. Messrs. Parke and Davis recognized the value of his work, and in 1883, announced a list of 20 standardized "normal liquids." Parke-Davis also pioneered in developing pharmacologic and physiologic standards for pharmaceuticals.

153

whereby Meyer's reagent was used for the determination of the alkaloids concerned. In recent days most of the pharmacopoeias have presented methods for the determination of alkaloids in tinctures and extracts, simultaneously fixing a definite amount of these alkaloids as the 'standard.'

"This German statement, recognizing (although somewhat grudgingly) the Anglo-Saxon priority in the realization of the idea of standardization of 'drugs, tinctures and extracts,' leaves the question open in which of the two countries concerned the first steps were taken. The answer was given by Frank O. Taylor in 1914 in an article, 'Forty-Five Years of Manufacturing Pharmacy,' published in the *Journal of the American Pharmaceutical Association*, vol. IV, pp. 468-481. It was the laboratories of Parke, Davis & Company, Detroit, to which the credit goes, and it was a man with personal experience in almost all branches of pharmacy—as a teacher, author, editor, analytical and consulting chemist, for several years owner of a prescription pharmacy—Albert Brown Lyons, M.D., (1841-1926) who was largely responsible for the early standardization work. To quote from F. O. Taylor's article:

" 'As the activity in the search for new drugs began to wane, there appeared the forerunner of what, it seems to me, is the most important advance in pharmacy that has occurred in modern times, the application of the principle of standardization, or uniformity in production of preparations of drugs. With no flourish of trumpets and little realization of what it heralded, in September, 1879, there appeared a preparation known as *Liquor Ergotae Purificatus*, which was a fluid preparation of ergot, standardized by a simple form of assay so that each different lot was of uniform character . . . With this there began a systematic investigation of the possibility of rendering uniform, fluid preparations of many drugs with the result that in February, 1883, there was publicly announced a list of twenty normal liquids which were actually fluid extracts standardized by some form of assay, in most cases an estimation of the alkaloids which they contained. The man responsible for the beginning of these assayed fluid extracts, and who established the analytical methods for their control is **Dr. A. B. Lyons**, to whom in this, as in many other things, pharmacy owes much . . . It is worthy of notice that the work instituted by this firm (Parke, Davis & Company) and followed in later years by a host of helpers has always kept far in advance of the official requirements of the various pharmacopoeias as they have been established.'

"In the United States it was the seventh decennial revision of the *United States Pharmacopoeia*, published in 1893; in England the *British Pharmacopoeia* of 1885; which introduced, for the first time, the assay and standardization of drugs and galenical preparations. 'This probably was,' says James Grier, 'a main factor in discouraging the pharmacist from making his own galenicals as hitherto.' The question whether, in this special case, the development of large scale production was to be welcomed or not, was answered by Frederick Hoffmann of New York in his German language journal, the *Pharmaceutische Rundschau* (vol. VIII, 1890, p. 62) in a way which is of general validity and importance.

" 'That pharmaceutical large scale manufacturers have already started to solve the problem (of standardization),' Hoffmann said, 'which had been recognized by pharmacology and therapy and was anyway within the sphere of their tasks and interests, and that they have been trying their very best to achieve the utmost that could be achieved at this time, does by no means justify the rather frequent attacks hurled against them by pharmacists. On the contrary, as far as this endeavor is based on scientific and rational consideration it deserves recognition and promotion. This effort, asking for synchronization of the results of chemical and pharmaceutical research and the progress made in the field of pharmacology, is open to everyone . . . Whoever precedes in this way is rendering a great service to the public welfare as well as to medicine in particular and will conquer the market.' "

Albert Brown Lyons was born in Waimea, Hawaii, April 1, 1841, the son of a missionary. He received education at Oahu College, and graduated in medicine from the University of

Michigan. He also studied pharmaceutical chemistry under Professor A. B. Prescott. After receiving his M.D. degree, he became assistant to Professor Samuel P. Duffield, who then occupied the Chair of Chemistry at the Detroit College of Medicine —the same Dr. Duffield who in 1862 began the small manufacturing business that became Parke, Davis & Company.

Dr. Lyons succeeded Professor Duffield, becoming Professor of Chemistry in 1869. This position he held for twelve years. About the same time, he also launched a retail pharmacy, which he operated for some ten years.

In 1881, Dr. Lyons severed these connections to accept a position with Parke, Davis & Company as analytical and consulting chemist, which he held until 1888. While there he became interested in the importance of standardization of drug preparations, and worked out assays for the "normal liquids" the company released in 1883.

Many publications came from the pen of Dr. Lyons, most important of which were the *Manual of Pharmaceutical Assaying*, (1887) and *Plant Names, Scientific and Popular*. He served as first editor of the *Pharmaceutical Era*. He also was a member of the U.S.P. Revision Committees of 1900 and 1910.

In 1888, Dr. Lyons accepted a position in Honolulu as government chemist for the Hawaiian Islands; and also as professor of chemistry at Oahu College. Returning to Detroit in 1897, he took charge of the chemical department of Nelson, Baker & Company, which position he held until poor health forced his retirement in 1912. He was named Honorary President of The American Pharmaceutical Association in 1915.

Parke, Davis & Company also is credited with establishment, in 1895, of the first pharmacologic laboratory in a pharmaceutical house. Two well-trained scientific men were placed in charge— C. T. McClintock, M.D., and E. M. Houghton, M.D. To Dr. Houghton properly belongs credit for pioneering and establishing the principles of physiologic standardization of drug preparations. He foresaw the importance and possibilities of this practical application of pharmacology long before its significance was generally recognized by others. Of this milestone in the improvement of quality and reliability of drugs, Dr. Taylor says:

"As an extension of the work of standardization of drugs and their preparations, there appeared . . . the first fluids that were standardized by physiological assay as distinct from any chemical assay. It is an interesting coincidence that the first fluid so standardized was also the first one whose uniform production had been attempted by a chemical assay—fluid extract of ergot (1897). Following this there came, at intervals, (physiologically) standardized products of a number of other drugs, such as the various heart tonics . . ."

First drugs specifically studied by Dr. Houghton were ergot, cannabis, the digitalis group, and strophanthus.

The significance of the work of Dr. Lyons, and later, of Dr. Houghton, is almost immeasurable. Examined in the light of the knowledge gained in the next three quarters of a century, Dr. Lyons' assay methods seem crude and inadequate; and Dr. Houghton's methods have been discarded for much-improved successors. However, it was their destiny to point the way for other research scientists to follow. It is from this pioneer leadership, rather than from specific personal accomplishments, that Pharmacy, Medicine, and the public whom they serve, have benefited most.

WRESTING
THE JUNGLE'S SECRETS

EXPEDITIONS in search of new plants that might have useful medicinal properties probably are as old as Pharmacy itself. Certainly they were not new undertakings in the days of Theophrastus (288 B.C.) or Dioscorides (77 A.D.), although these early writers contributed much knowledge that was new. Nor were such pharmaceutical explorations entirely the province of the nineteenth century scientific adventurers who opened vast new horizons for the advancement of Pharmacy and Medicine of that day—of whom, according to Urdang, Dr. Henry Hurd Rusby (1855-1940) was undoubtedly the most outstanding.

Tschirch, in his monumental *Handbuch der Pharmakognosie*, devotes fifty-six pages (chapter XXV) to a discussion of these exploits.

"Nothing," says Tschirch, "has promoted our knowledge of drugs more than the voyages of discovery . . . While pharmacognosy in the Middle Ages had become a philological science, it developed into a scientific discipline . . . The discovery of the all water route to the East Indies (in 1498) brought about an increase and a deepening of our knowledge of drugs which had been known before. The discovery of America extended the materia medica as such in a most unexpected way."

Stating that the period between the end of the fifteenth and the early sixteenth century has been called "the age of discoveries," Tschirch contends that "for pharmacognosy it really was a new time, not a mere Renaissance as had been the case in the arts and sciences (in general)."

Spices and effective drugs being highly priced, they meant riches and power for those who commanded the routes leading to these countries of plenty. To quote again from Tschirch:

"During the seventeenth and eighteenth centuries the great

WRESTING THE JUNGLE'S SECRETS

Expeditions in search of new medicinal plants probably are as old as Pharmacy. Scientific adventurers, such as Henry Hurd Rusby (1855-1940), opened vast new horizons for the advancement of Pharmacy and Medicine, late in the nineteenth century. Sent by Parke, Davis & Company in 1884 to Peru for supplies of coca leaves, Dr. Rusby crossed the Andes and journeyed down the Amazon to the Atlantic amid incredible hardships. He returned with 45,000 botanical specimens. Among them were many new drug plants, including cocillana bark, pharmaceutical preparations of which are still important to Medicine. Dr. Rusby later became Dean of the College of Pharmacy of Columbia University.

fights took place among the seafaring nations for the monopoly of the trade in spices and, consequently, for the domination over the seas and the ways of international trade in general. These fights started between Portugal and Spain and were later continued particularly between Holland, England, and France. It was the time of the special commercial agencies which, bestowed with all possible privileges by their governments, carried on the task of exploitation with a recklessness unheard of before and often characterized by an unparalleled cruelty toward the natives concerned. Hence political and commercial mismanagement prepared the ground for the ruin of this kind of colonization . . ."

Botanical and pharmacognostical research, sponsored by the young and growing manufacturing branch of Pharmacy, reached their peak in the latter quarter of the nineteenth century. Dr. Frank O. Taylor, in his article, "Forty-five Years of Manufacturing Pharmacy," written in 1914 (*Journal of the American Pharmaceutical Association*), describes one facet of this movement:

"It may surprise you . . . to find how many drugs were originally brought to the attention of the medical profession by this young firm . . .

"In the course of these investigations, Parke, Davis & Company, through representatives, explored the northern parts of California, Washington, Oregon, British Columbia, and Mexico. One representative (Count Hansen) was sent to the Fiji Islands to obtain a supply of the drug Tonga; another going to the West Indies brought back Jamaica Dogwood and a few other less important drugs. A special representative, dispatched in 1881, made a trip from the mouth of the Amazon River about 2500 miles into the interior, and as a result of this expedition the drug Manaca was added to the growing list of new remedial agents. About the same time another representative proceeded inland from Buenos Aires on horseback clear across the mountain range to the Pacific coast. This work resulted in the discovery of the herb Chekan, and the obtaining of supplies of Boldo, Quebracho, and some other Chilean drugs. In 1885, Dr. H. H. Rusby made an extensive trip in South America, in the interests of Parke, Davis & Company, as a result of which he brought back much scientific information and among many other plants the drugs Pichi and Cocillana, together with extensive supplies of Coca from Peru."

Dr. Rusby did not begin his life's training in Pharmacy. He was by inclination and study a botanist and a teacher; but it was in the field of Pharmacy that he gave a lifetime of service. There are conflicting reports of his adventurous, and not infrequently, controversial, career. One that seems eminently fair appeared in *The New York Times* of November 19, 1940, the day after Dr. Rusby's death, from which we quote:

"His career began at the age of 10 when he was on the farm of his father, John Rusby, near Franklin, New Jersey, where he was born on April 26, 1855. The village school teacher introduced him, casually, to the study of botany, and he spent all his spare time collecting the flora of New Jersey's woods.

"In 1872 he entered the Massachusetts State Normal School and took up the study in earnest. At the Centennial Exposition of 1876 (in Philadelphia) he won a medal for his herbarium of plants of Essex County, New Jersey. He had left the normal school in 1874 and for a year studied at the College of Physicians and Surgeons at Columbia University, but the financial misfortunes of his father caused him to withdraw.

"He persuaded the Smithsonian Institution to appoint him an agent, and in 1880, 1881 and again in 1883, he headed an expedition into the Southwest to collect plants. He was once robbed by a Mexican bandit and had many brushes with the Apache Indians.

"Desiring to further his education, he wrote to Parke, Davis & Company, Detroit drug manufacturers, and said he wanted to work for them. They offered to put him through college in this country and in Europe if he agreed to work for them for five years after graduation. Instead he sold them his herbarium for $40 a month for the rest of his college course. He was graduated from the University Medical College of New York University in 1884.

"Shortly after graduation, his employers asked him one Friday how soon he could start for South America. He offered to go Monday. The properties of cocaine had just been discovered, and on this short notice the young Dr. Rusby set off for Bolivia, where he soon had collected 20,000 pounds of the (coca) leaf. This, valued at $250,000, was lost in a revolution in Colombia. Parke, Davis & Company cabled him to come home.

"Instead, Dr. Rusby collected a crew of soldiers of fortune and started into the then strange country of the Amazon's headwaters. Several months later, with 45,000 specimens, many hundreds of which were unknown to botany, he staggered more dead than alive onto the grounds of E. S. Rand, orchid expert, at Para (on the Atlantic coast). The incredulous Rand thought he had been killed long since by the Indians, had sought him in the wilds and had cabled news of his death to Detroit. When finally Dr. Rusby returned to his father's home in Nutley (New Jersey), his father failed to recognize him, so ravaged was he by the rigors and diseases of the jungle."

It was during the eastern Andean portion of this journey, at a fairly high altitude in a tropical rain-forest, near Guanai, that Dr. Rusby collected specimens of Guapi, or cocillana bark. The jungle's secrets could be obtained only by hacking his way literally foot by foot with his machete, carrying his herb press on his back. When the rain-forest's flora was conquered, its fauna and insectivora still remained to be dealt with.

From incredible hardships such as those which confronted Dr. Rusby came many new pharmaceutical preparations that gave aid and comfort to the sick. Despite the rapid therapeutic advances of the middle decades of the twentieth century, a number of the botanical drugs discovered on Rusby's expedition, particularly cocillana, still are of importance as therapeutic agents.

Following his return from South America, Dr. Rusby resumed

his service with Parke, Davis & Company, giving many lectures on his travels. In 1888, he became Professor of Botany, Physiology, and Materia Medica in the College of Pharmacy of the City of New York. Thus began a new phase of his career, in which he was to gain further fame—and stir up controversy. He became dean of the College in 1905; and it was under his leadership that the College became affiliated with Columbia University. Dr. Rusby continued as dean of the College of Pharmacy until 1930, when he retired.

Dr. Rusby joined The American Pharmaceutical Association in 1889, and served it in many capacities, including its presidency in 1910. In 1890, he was elected to membership on the Revision Committee of the *United States Pharmacopoeia*, serving on its seventh, eighth, and ninth revisions. He also served as a member of the Committee on the *National Formulary* for many years. He was very active in cooperation with Dr. Harvey Wiley in the crusade for the enactment of the Pure Food and Drug law, and in helping to vindicate Dr. Wiley when efforts were made to remove him from his office in charge of the enforcement of that law.

On several occasions during his teaching career, Dr. Rusby took time out to lead expeditions into little known areas of South America and Mexico. His last, in 1921 and 1922, was sponsored by the pharmaceutical firm of H. K. Mulford Company, of Philadelphia. Before completion of this expedition, however, poor health forced him to return ahead of his party.

In 1933, Dr. Rusby published a book entitled *Jungle Memories*, in which he told "the story of but a single expedition—the transcontinental journey of 1885-1887," which he considered to be "one of the most important from a scientific standpoint."

Despite his vigorous life, and the poor health of his later years, Dr. Rusby lived to be eighty-five years old. His death came on November 18, 1940.

Pharmaceutical exploration did not end with the nineteenth century, nor with Rusby. It still continues, despite the competition of chemotherapy. An international association for promoting the cultivation and utilization of plants used for medicinal purposes and as spices was founded in Vienna in 1927. After an interruption during the second World War it has become active again. One of the founders, Professor Richard Wasicky, former Dean of the Department of Pharmacognosy at the University of Vienna, who found a new place of work at the University of Sao Paulo in Brazil, has created an institution for searching out botanical drugs, then isolating and later synthesizing the important ingredients. This work has been put on an international basis by Dr. Wasicky. The role of plants as remedial agents has changed—not in relation to their potential for therapeutic good, but in the methods by which these qualities are made available for use by Pharmacy and Medicine.

WORLD EVENTS AND PHARMACY HISTORY

Dates, persons, and events of significance to the evolution of Pharmacy include:

1908	Kamerlingh Onnes liquefied helium.
1908	Paul Ehrlich and Elie Metchnikoff shared Nobel prize for work in immunity.
1908	Zeppelin constructed improved airship.
1908	Cushing operated on the pituitary gland.
1908	Peking Union Medical College founded by Rockefeller Institute.
1908	American Public Health Association standardized tests for milk.
1908-10	William Pasteur described massive (postoperative) collapse of the lungs.
1909	Sorensen investigated hydrogen ion concentration.
1909	Hofmann synthesized caoutchouc (india rubber).
1909	F. F. Russell vaccinated United States Army against typhoid fever.
1909	Nobel prize awarded to Kocher for his contribution on the thyroid gland.
1909-13	Marine and Lenhart standardized iodine treatment of goiter.
1910	Flexner produced poliomyelitis experimentally.
1910	Abraham Flexner published survey of medical schools and education.
1910	Vedder demonstrated amebicidal action of emetine.
1910	Chapin, Winslow, and Robinson emphasized danger of contact infection in communicable diseases.
1910	Ehrlich and Hata introduced salvarsan (606).
1910	Nobel prize awarded to Albrecht Kossel for his work on cellular chemistry.
1910-27	A. V. Hill investigated thermodynamics of muscular contraction.
1911	Cushing described dyspituitarism.
1911	Walter Cannon published *The Mechanical Factors of Digestion*.
1911	Peyton Rous (U.S.) showed cancer in chickens caused by virus.
1911	Nobel prizes awarded to Marie Curie and A. Gullstrand for their respective works on radiation chemistry and dioptrics of the eye.
1911-14	Casimir Funk investigated vitamines.
1911-15	Van Slyke devised methods of estimating amino nitrogen and amino acids.
1911-27	Pavlov investigated conditional reflexes.
1912	Nicolle, Anderson, and Goldberger produced experimental typhus in monkey.
1912	Joseph Lister died.
1912	Weber and Lorey effected x-ray examination of abdominal viscera (pneumoperitoneum).
1912	Von Behring employed toxin-antitoxin immunization against diphtheria.
1912	Nobel prize awarded to Alexis Carrel for his work on organ transplantation and vascular suturing.
1912-13	Gustav Embden and co-workers investigated carbohydrate metabolism.
1912-14	Institut du Radium (Curie Foundation) erected at Paris.
1912-16	Cannon investigated effect of adrenal secretion on emotions.
1913	Schick introduced susceptibility test for diphtheria.
1913	Vitamin A discovered.
1913	Krönig and Gauss introduced morphine-scopolamine anesthesia in obstetrics (twilight sleep).
1913	Douglas, Haldane, Henderson, and Schneider investigated effect of acclimatization to high altitudes (Pike's Peak) on respiration.
1913	Wellcome Medical and Medico-Historical Museums (London) founded.
1913	Rockefeller Foundation (New York) chartered.
1913	Nobel prize awarded to Charles Richet for his work on anaphylaxis.
1913-16	Dochez, Gillespie, and Avery typed the pneumococci.
1913-16	McCollum, Davis, and Kennedy described vitamins A and B.
1913-27	Maude Slye experimented on hereditary susceptibility to and immunity from cancer.

STANISLAS LIMOUSIN
PHARMACAL INVENTOR

PROGRESS of the human race through the ages has been advanced on many occasions by application of the scientific knowledge and technical skill required in the practice of Pharmacy. Combine with these factors a curious, probing, and inventive mind—and the world surely will have gained.

One person so singularly gifted was the French retail pharmacist, Stanislas Limousin (1831-1887). In his pharmacy on Blanche Street in Paris, his spare time was continually taken up with experimentation. He sought ways to solve the vexing problems confronting the professions of Pharmacy and Medicine. From the practical discoveries he made there came developments that saved countless lives, and made untold millions of sick persons more comfortable.

Among the many devices introduced to the health professions by Pharmacist Limousin are the medicine dropper; the identification of poisons, especially arsenic and corrosive sublimate, by distinctive colors; and the wafer cachet. From Limousin's time until past the turn of the twentieth century, when manufacture of hard gelatin capsules became practical on a massive scale, cachets, consisting of doses of powdered medicines sealed between two thin rice-starch shells, were a welcome advance in pharmaceutical technique. Many a disagreeable-tasting prescription was made acceptable by this innovation of the Parisian apothecary; and cachet-sealing machines were a part of the equipment of every pharmacy.

World fame, however, came to Limousin because of the apparatus which he designed for the therapeutic administration of oxygen; and because of his invention of the ampoule.

Albert Goris, in a pamphlet written in honor of Limousin (supplement to *La Pharmacie Française*, March and April, 1939),

STANISLAS LIMOUSIN—PHARMACAL INVENTOR

One of those persons singularly gifted in combining scientific knowledge with technical skill and inventive genius was the French retail pharmacist, Stanislas Limousin (1831-1887). Among the many devices which he introduced to Pharmacy and Medicine were the medicine dropper; the system of coloring poisons (such as corrosive sublimate); and wafer cachets (which found favor prior to mass production of the gelatin capsule). His greatest contributions, however, were the development and perfection of apparatus for the inhalation and therapeutic administration of oxygen; and invention of glass ampoules that could be sealed and sterilized for preservation of solutions for hypodermic use.

discusses these achievements. The following are literal quotations from Goris' paper:

"It was his work concerning the inhalation of oxygen which drew the attention of the medical profession to the young pharmacist who had established himself at Blanche Street in Paris. Moreover, it has to be stated that, from 1866 to his death, Limousin never ceased working on the therapeutic utilization of the gas.

"The first attempts at the medical application of oxygen go back to the time of the discovery of the gas by Priestley, who examined the physiologic effect on mice and on himself. In 1832, during the cholera epidemic, some physicians at various places tried to utilize the gas, without much success, against this disease. Later, the investigation of Paul Bert, made from a physiological rather than a medical vantage point, again drew attention to the gas.

"In 1864, Demarquay and Leonte, after a profound study of the effect of oxygen on the organism, were most desirous of introducing this gas into therapy. They encountered great difficulties, however, because of the absence of a convenient and practical method for the preparation, collection and administration of the oxygen."

After having described how Limousin solved these problems and step by step improved the apparatus (consisting in part of balloon-like bags), Goris goes on to say:

"These balloons are still actually in use . . . The consumption of this gas for medical purposes is considerable and it is undoubtedly the initiative of Limousin to which we are indebted for the development of this kind of therapy. He was not content with having been a fortunate manipulator, but pursued physiological investigations concerning the elimination of carbon monoxide in connection with the oxygen inhalation. He indicated precautions to be taken in order to avoid the regrettable accidents which had happened . . .

"Limousin was directly involved in an unfortunate accident following the ascension of the balloon Zenith in 1874. On the occasion of a previous ascension, Paul Bert had furnished the aeronauts with the means to combat the enfeeblement and asphyxia otherwise befalling the fliers in higher altitudes, thus, thanks to artificial respiration, enabling them to reach 7400 metres without inconvenience.

"Croce-Spinnelli, Sivel, and G. Tissandier asked Limousin—who was to accompany them and was in the last moment prevented from doing so—to furnish them with oxygen balloons . . . Due to the too rapid ascension and the premature syncope of the aeronauts, the inhalations could not be applied at the opportune time. This default caused the death of Croce-Spinelli and of Sivel; G. Tissandier, not having succumbed to a sudden syncope, retained his respiratory movements thanks to a small quantity of oxygen which he had inhaled somewhat earlier."

As sad as this accident was, there could not be any better advertising of the effect of oxygen inhalation.

Limousin in all probability was the first to establish special conveniences for the therapeutic use of oxygen. It was in a special room of his pharmacy that, as early as 1874, these conveniences were offered to the public. The first two paragraphs of the prospectus in which Limousin announced this venture read as follows:

"I have established in my pharmacy, 2 Blanche Street, with an entrance through Saint-Lazare Street, a special room for inhalation to which the physicians may bring or send the patients whom they want to be subjected to oxygen gas inhalations.

"There in the morning from 9 to 11, and in the evening from 3 to 5, the patients, presented by their physicians or provided with a prescription, will be received. They will then, under my supervision, inhale the prescribed dosage of the oxygen gas."

Although the use of oxygen as a general therapeutic means did not meet the original expectations, its value as a lifesaver has remained unchallenged. "Who, being severely sick," says Goris, "has not become acquainted with the oxygen balloon?"

Limousin's wide range of research and development is further revealed by this commentator: "Hypodermic medication," continues Goris, "having been made fashionable by Dujardin-Beaumetz, the medical profession (and still more, the pharmaceutical profession), looked for means for the conservation of the solutions to be injected. The simple aqueous solutions, prepared in advance, had the great disadvantage of deteriorating rapidly through the development of mold. Furthermore, the volume of the containers made their transportation inconvenient . . . At the instigation of Dr. Duhomme, President of the Société Thérapeutique, Limousin indicated a simple solution of the problem."

Limousin's glass *ampoules hypodermiques* removed these inconveniences. In his classical essay, *Ampoules hypodermiques; nouveau mode de préparation des solutions hypodermiques*, published in 1886 in the *Archives of Pharmacy*, he described his method which, in principle, has remained the same up to the present, as follows:

"These ampoules have the form of a small ovoid balloon. They are terminated by a tapered glass tube, and their capacity is a little greater than one cc.

"I sterilize the inside of these small containers, using the method of M. Pasteur, by submitting them in an oven to a temperature of about 200 degrees (celsius). I then fill them with the medicated solution, be it by introducing the point of the hot ampoule into the cold liquid, or be it by injecting the hot liquid by means of a small injector at the highest point of the ampoule.

"The ampoule being filled, I close it over the oxidation flame by holding the open end of the tube into the uppermost part of the flame."

With this classic simplicity, Pharmacist Limousin outlined the essential directions for the manufacture of ampoules. Though great advances have been made since in the techniques and mechanics of ampoule production, Limousin's simple rules are still the basic, underlying principles. Thus, a new and important means of administration of medicines was stabilized and made safe for use by physicians for the benefit of millions of patients.

Stanislas Limousin did not live to see the enormous growth and application of his invention, for he died one year after the publication of his essay on *ampoules hypodermiques*. Nor did he see the great improvements on and expansion of his techniques for the inhalation of oxygen, and their application to other therapeutic gases. There is no doubt, however, of the debt that mankind owes to this modest retail pharmacist.

WORLD EVENTS AND PHARMACY HISTORY

Dates, persons, and events of significance to the evolution of Pharmacy include:

1914	Christiansen, Douglas, and Haldane investigated CO_2 carriage by the blood.
1914	Panama Canal opened.
1914	St. Petersburg became Petrograd.
1914	Nobel prize awarded to Robert Bárány for his work on the vestibular apparatus.
1914-18	World War I.
1914-19	E. C. Kendall discovered and investigated thyroxin.
1915	Carrel-Dakin treatment of infected (gunshot) wounds.
1915	Walter Cannon published *Bodily Changes in Pain, Hunger, Fear, and Rage.*
1915	Delousing of troops organized.
1915	Paul Ehrlich died.
1915	Twort reported on bacteriophages.
1915	Preventive inoculation against tetanus in gunshot wounds.
1915	Simmonds described pituitary dwarfism.
1915	Joseph Goldberger demonstrated that pellagra results from nutritional deficiency.
1915-16	Mott *et al.* investigated shell shock.
1916	Bull introduced antitoxin for gas gangrene.
1916	Vitamin B (complex) discovered.
1916	The Johns Hopkins School of Hygiene and Public Health opened.
1917	Ruth Tunnicliff discovered diplococcus in measles.
1917	Wagner von Jauregg treated paresis by superinfection with malarial fever.
1917	Windaus extracted cholesterin (vitamin D) from cod liver oil and formulated it.
1917	Vitamin D reported.
1917-18	American commission investigated trench fever.
1918	Fahraeus introduced erythrocyte sedimentation test.
1918	Ellerman established transmission of leukemia in chickens by virus.
1918-19	Spanish influenza pandemic.
1918-24	Flexner, Amoss, and Webster investigated experimental epidemiology.
1919	Mellanby produced experimental rickets.
1919	Huldschinsky demonstrated antirachitic effect of ultraviolet light.
1919	Huldschinsky demonstrated curative effect of sunlight (quartz lamp) on rickets.
1919	Kolle and Ritz treated experimental (rabbit) syphilis with bismuth.
1919	Dale and Laidlaw investigated histamine shock.
1919	E. Mellanby treated experimental rickets with cod liver oil.
1919	Nobel prize awarded to Bordet for his contributions on immunity.
1920	E. C. Cutler (U.S.) and P. W. Souttar (England) performed heart surgery.
1920	Paul Saxl (Austria) introduced mercurial diuretics for treatment of cardiac edema.
1920	Nobel prize awarded to August Krogh for his discovery of the capillary motor regulator mechanism.
1921	Banting and Best isolated insulin.
1921	A. F. Hess treated rickets by exposure to sunlight.
1921	General use of iodine as an antiseptic (Pregl's solution).
1921	Institut Behring (for Experimental Therapy) at Marburg.
1921-26	R. L. Kahn introduced serum test for syphilis.
1922	Petrograd became Leningrad.
1922	McCollum and Steenbock discovered vitamin D.

THE ERA OF BIOLOGICALS

THE ERA of biologicals (medicinal preparations made from microorganisms and their products) traditionally is thought of as having its start in 1894, following the International Congress of Hygiene in Budapest. It was at this meeting that the German scientist Behring and the French scientist Roux presented clear-cut evidence of the clinical value of antidiphtheritic serum. Within a year, manufacture of the serum was begun, and distribution set up through normal pharmaceutical channels. However, this had been preceded by ten years of intensive research by Loeffler, Roux and Yersin, and Ehrlich and Behring. In fact, Behring had published papers both on the discovery of tetanus antitoxin and on immunization against diphtheria in 1890. However, the use of biological products for the benefit of mankind sprang from roots planted more than 100 years earlier. According to Urdang:

"The idea of artificially induced immunity against contagious diseases was outlined by the English physican, Edward Jenner (1749-1823). On May 14, 1796, Jenner, leaning on earlier empiric observations and the conclusions he had drawn, dared his first practical experiment. It was a full success, proving beyond any doubt that the technique of 'inoculation,' i.e., the induction of some fluid from a smallpox pustule in a superficial incision in the arm, which had been used up to that date, had to be replaced by 'vaccination,' i.e., the induction of cowpox. While the first method was not without some danger—and above all—did not offer itself for mass application, the method of Jenner met both requirements, thus putting an end to the spread of the devastating disease. When Jenner, in 1798, published a booklet of 75 pages and 4 tables, entitled 'An Inquiry Into the Causes and Effects of the Variolae Vaccine, a disease discovered in some of the Western

172

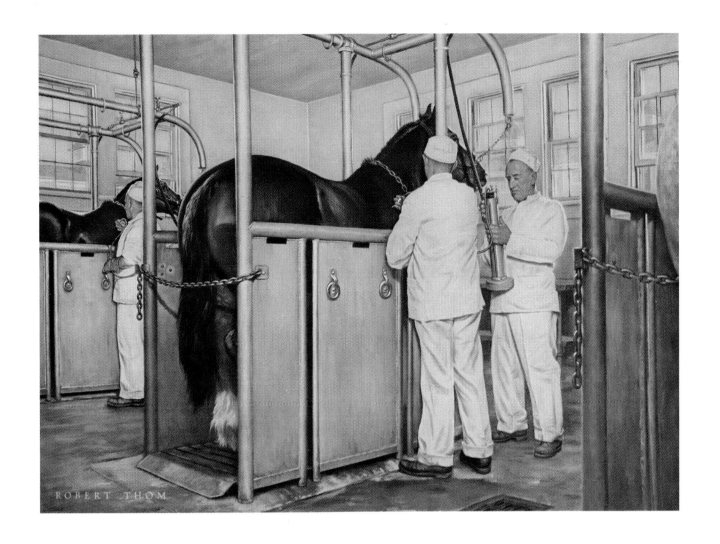

THE ERA OF BIOLOGICALS

When, in 1894, Behring and Roux announced the effectiveness of diphtheria antitoxin,

pharmaceutical scientists both in Europe and in the United States rushed to put the new dis-

covery into production. Parke, Davis & Company was among the pioneers. The serum

became available in 1895, and lives of thousands of children were saved. Inoculation of

horses with diphtheria toxin was the first step of many in producing antitoxin. Parke-

Davis received U. S. Biological License No. 1 in 1903. New, improved biological

products have continued to become available, climaxed in 1955 by poliomyelitis vaccine.

Counties of England, particularly Gloucestershire,' the battle was won.

"This courageous and eminently fruitful deed received scientific support with the discovery of the laws of bacteriology by the French chemist, Louis Pasteur (1822-1897); by the German physicians Robert Koch (1843-1910), and Emil von Behring (1854-1917). To Pasteur we are indebted for the methods of employing cultures of weakened bacteria, the vaccines; for his demonstration of the existence of sickness-producing germs in the air, and especially, for the discovery of sterilization and pasteurization—the knowledge and technic by which microorganisms and their spores can be destroyed by heat and other means. To Koch we owe, in addition to the discovery of a series of morbific agents, the modern technic of bacteriology; and to Behring the knowledge of how to produce antitoxins in the blood serum of animals by inoculating them with specific toxins.

"There were two factors which made the work of Behring so particularly effective as well as dramatic: (1) the sickness which he attacked first was diphtheria, known for thousands of years as an irresistible killer of children; and (2) the methods worked out by Paul Ehrlich (1854-1919) allowing an exact determination of the value of the serum.

"The success of this first serum was so obvious that even skeptics like Virchow had to admit it. No wonder that Behring received the most enthusiastic expressions of gratitude. The people called him 'the saviour of children.' He received the first Nobel Prize for medicine, and his king made him a member of the Prussian nobility. The second serum prepared by Behring, his 'tetanus antitoxin,' was likewise a full success . . .

"Mr. von Behring was not only a great scientist and a very ambitious gentleman, but a man who knew the value of money. He established at Marburg and Bremen plants for the manufacture of his serums, and died a wealthy man."

Immediately after that historic Congress in Budapest, there was a flurry of activity both in Europe and America to begin large-scale production of the much needed antidiphtheritic serum. Apparently the first to be released in the United States was made under the supervision of the Board of Health of New York City. Parke, Davis & Company of Detroit, Michigan, also acted quickly. Dr. E. M. Houghton, writing in the *Bulletin of the Wayne County Medical Society* in 1921 ("Dr. Charles Thomas McClintock, A Memorial"), states that:

"Immediately after the announcement of the discovery of diphtheria antitoxin by Behring and Roux, in the autumn of 1894, he (Dr. McClintock) was invited by Parke, Davis & Company to organize and equip a laboratory for the manufacture of diphtheria antitoxin, which was the first or one of the first institutions of its kind in America. It was soon recognized that a new chapter in prophylactic and curative medicine had been opened, demanding the investigation and elucidation of innumerable questions . . . ."

At its beginning, "the department was in the charge of Charles T. McClintock, A.M., M.D., Ph.D.; Karl Schwickerath, Ph.G., Ph.D.; and George Suttie, Ph.C., M.D. By 1896, it was under the supervision of McClintock and Houghton . . ." both of whom had come from the University of Michigan.

In his *History of Wayne County and the City of Detroit, Michigan*, Clarence M. Burton offers this comment:

"No expectation of profit prompted the beginning in 1894 of the great Parke-Davis laboratories now devoted to the production of antitoxic serums . . . Mr. Davis, then general manager, entered the biological field solely in a spirit of scientific enterprise. He undoubtedly expected credit and reputation but not revenue from this venture . . ."

According to a memorandum, dated August 9, 1898, written by Dr. Houghton, the preparation and testing of diphtheria toxins and the necessary experimental work in the production of diphtheria antitoxins began at Parke-Davis in November, 1894. The first horse was injected with diphtheria toxin, January 7, 1895, and the first blood was drawn from an immunized horse on March 22, 1895. Meantime, according to a statement in the June, 1895, issue of *Pharmacal Notes* (forerunner of *Modern Pharmacy*), Parke-Davis was "happy to announce our ability to supply on demand quantities of Diphtheria Antitoxin . . . prepared under the supervision of Ira Van Gieson, M.D., and Nelson L. Deming, M.D., well known bacteriological experts of New York City, and issued under their certificate of quality and strength . . . (which) conforms to . . . the ordinance of the Board of Health of New York City . . ." This was available in three strengths—a 600-unit vial for immunizing purposes; a 1000-unit vial, and a 1500-unit vial, for curative uses. Parke-Davis began marketing its own antitoxin shortly thereafter. By 1896, *Pharmacal Notes* announced that the following products were being manufactured: antidiphtheritic serum (four different potencies), antitetanic serum, antistreptococcic serum, antitubercle serum, erysipelas and prodigiosus toxins, and Coley's mixture of both toxins, as well as eight kinds of culture media, and microscopic slides of disease germs. In 1898, glycerinated smallpox vaccine was announced.

Of this fast-moving period, Dr. F. O. Taylor (*Journal of the A.Ph.A.*), says: "In 1898 appeared, for the first time, a package containing 3000 units (of antidiphtheritic serum), and from this time on, for some time, the strength of dosage was not greatly increased, but the effort was made to cut down the amount (of serum) necessary to obtain the same potency . . . The first serum made contained about fifty to sixty antitoxic units per cc., but very quickly the strength of the serum was increased . . ."

Another interesting phase of the diphtheria antitoxin development was in packaging. First packaged in corked vials, the serum soon lost its potency. By September, 1896, Parke-Davis was advertising the product in hermetically sealed, globular-shaped, stemmed glass vials. By August, 1903, the serum was offered in a bulb syringe with a sterile needle. By October of that year, a piston-syringe container was available.

Meantime, von Behring was not idle. Besides building commercial serum manufacturing plants in Germany, in January, 1895, he applied for a United States patent on the manufacture of diphtheria antitoxin. Five such applications were denied; but in June, 1898, a patent was finally granted von Behring.

This created a furor in American pharmaceutical circles. Parke, Davis & Company and the H. K. Mulford Company, leading U. S. manufacturers of diphtheria antitoxin, announced to their customers that they would fight the patent in the courts. Fortunately, however, von Behring did not make any serious attempt at enforcing his U. S. patent.

Nor were these early days of serum manufacture without their headaches. The front page of the December 12, 1897, *New York Journal* carried a headline:

ANTITOXIN THAT KILLS WHERE IT SHOULD CURE

The story that followed was to have an amazing parallel in the newspaper headlines in the middle of 1955, when another biological product, poliomyelitis vaccine, was for a time suspected as a killer. In both instances, investigation revealed more hysteria than fact.

The 1897 developments led to a governmental inspection and licensing system. On August 21, 1903, Parke, Davis & Company was issued License No. 1 "For the Manufacture of Viruses, Serums, Toxins, and Analogous Products" by the Treasury Department of the United States. It also was to receive License No. 1 from the Department of National Health and Welfare of Canada.

Progress in the development and manufacture of biological products was rapid after 1895. The first bacterial vaccine was announced in 1907. In 1908, Parke-Davis established the Parkedale Farm near Rochester, Michigan, for housing the many animals used in the production of antitoxins and other biological products. There, under the management of the veterinarian, Dr. R. H. Wilson, production of biologicals expanded greatly. By 1955, however, monkeys, rabbits and guinea pigs had largely replaced horses and heifers in importance at Parkedale, as intensive work on poliomyelitis vaccine got under way.

Time has dealt with biologicals much as it has with other

pharmaceuticals. The product of choice of one day is eclipsed by the improved products of the next.

Also, the effectiveness of preventive therapy has largely done away with the need for many curative biological products. Diseases such as diphtheria, which killed little children with a horrible death, and smallpox, have virtually disappeared, principally because of the general use of effective immunizing agents. Chemotherapeutic agents and the antibiotics have proved faster and more effective than serums in treatment of certain other illnesses.

The biological field still continues to be an important branch of Pharmacy. In 1955, following intensive efforts on the part of several leading biological manufacturing laboratories in cooperation with the National Foundation for Infantile Paralysis, a preventive vaccine against several strains of the causative agent of dread, crippling poliomyelitis, made its official appearance, with promise of retiring that virus-caused threat from prominence as a crippler and killer. Out of the polio vaccine research program also came hope that other virus-caused diseases eventually might be combated by techniques as new and thrilling as were those of Behring and Roux in 1894.

WORLD EVENTS AND PHARMACY HISTORY

Dates, persons, and events of significance to the evolution of Pharmacy include:

1922   Nobel prize awarded to Hill and Meyerhof for discoveries on heat production and metabolism of lactic acid in muscle tissue.

1923   George and Gladys Dick discovered hemolytic streptococcus of scarlatina and devised susceptibility test.

1923   Wilhelm Conrad Röntgen died.

1923   Graham and Cole introduced cholecystography (examination of gallbladder by x-rays).

1923   Nobel prize awarded to Banting and Macleod for insulin research.

1923   Gwathmey introduced synergistic anesthesia.

1924   History of Science Society (United States) founded at Boston.

1924   Nobel prize awarded to Einthoven for his discovery of the mechanism of the electrocardiogram.

1925   Whipple and Robschat-Robbins treated experimental anemia with raw liver.

1925   Sir Henry S. Soutar operated for mitral stenosis.

1926   Minot and Murphy introduced raw liver diet in pernicious anemia.

1926   Harvey Cushing received the Pulitzer prize for his *Life of Sir William Osler.*

1926   Vitamin B$_1$ isolated.

1926   C. R. Harington effected synthesis of thyroxin.

1926   E. L. Kennaway extracted first known cancer-causing chemical, 3, 4-benzpyrene.

1926   Collip isolated parathyroid hormone.

1926   Vitamins B$_1$ and B$_2$ described.

1926   Förster developed the brain-function chart.

1926   Busch developed electron optics.

1926   Nobel prize awarded to Fibiger for his discovery of the spiroptera carcinoma.

1927   Windaus identified ergosterol.

1927   Lindberg crossed Atlantic in aëroplane.

1927   Ramon (France) developed active immunization against tetanus; and later, diphtheria.

1927   Nobel prize awarded to Wagner-Jauregg for his use of malaria inoculation in treatment for dementia paralytica.

1928   Noguchi discovered pathogen of trachoma.

1928   Vitamin C (ascorbic acid) isolated.

1928   Penicillin discovered by Alexander Fleming (England).

1928   Forssmann performed the first heart catheterization.

1928   Nobel prize awarded to Windaus for vitamin research and Nicolle for his work on typhus fever.

1928   Raman reported on light dispersion of molecules.

1929   W. H. Welch appointed Professor of Medical History at The Johns Hopkins University.

1929   Joseph Goldberger died.

1929   Alexander Fleming announced discovery of penicillin.

1929   Hans Berger constructed the electroencephalograph.

1929   World-wide stock market crash— Black Friday.

1929   Nobel prize awarded to Eijkman and Hopkins for discoveries of antineuritic and growth-stimulating vitamins.

1930   Beginning of plastic chemistry.

1930   Nobel prize awarded to Landsteiner for discovery of human blood groups.

1930   Theiler developed immunization against yellow fever in animals.

1931   Vitamin K studied.

1931   Biotin described by György.

1931   Nobel prize awarded to Warburg for discovery of respiratory enzymes.

1931   Development of electron microscope.

1932   Gerhard Domagk (Germany) discovered prontosil (first of sulfa drugs).

1932   Riboflavin discovered.

1932   Chadwick discovered the neutron.

1932   Joliot-Curie discovered the positron.

1932   Urey discovered "heavy hydrogen."

1932   Lawrence developed the cyclotron.

1932   Zernike developed the phase-contrast microscope.

1932   Nobel prize awarded to Sherrington and Adrian for discovering the function of the neuron.

1932   High point of the depression. 30 million jobless. Beginning of Roosevelt era.

1933   Hitler rises to power in Germany. Beginning of the Third Reich.

1933   Nobel prize awarded to T. H. Morgan for his studies on chromosomes.

THE DEVELOPMENT
OF CHEMOTHERAPY

PHARMACY, as the profession having to do with the preparation and production of drugs for use by Medicine for the benefit
of mankind, entered into a vast new era at the close of the nineteenth century and the beginning of the twentieth. With the age
of biologicals barely launched, Pharmacy entered on the era of
chemotherapy (the direct attack on morbific agents in the body
by means of chemical substances).

Greatest stimulant of this transition was the rapid flow of new
discoveries coming from the great research laboratories, particularly in Europe. It became Pharmacy's problem to transform
the best of these discoveries from test-tube residues to tremendous
batches of thousands of pounds or thousands of gallons. The
product of this mass manufacture then had to be tested intensively,
in chemical and biological laboratories, and in clinics. The next
step was to expedite distribution, so that the finished medicines
might be readily available to fill physicians' prescriptions for ill
patients. This service could be regarded as satisfactory only when
it was available as close to the patient's home or bedside as the
community retail pharmacy.

Fulfilling its traditional role with remarkable facility in a time
of revolutionary transition, Pharmacy was to have its part in all
phases of this chemotherapeutic era; and pharmacists were to
have a part along with physicians, chemists, physicists, bacteriologists and many other workers in this vast new field of research.

One of the most successful researchers in the development of
new chemical compounds specifically created to fight disease-
causing organisms in the body was the French pharmacist, Ernest
François Auguste Fourneau (1872-1949).

M. Fourneau was apprenticed in 1889 in the pharmacy of Felix
Moureu in his natal city of Biarritz. He attended the École de

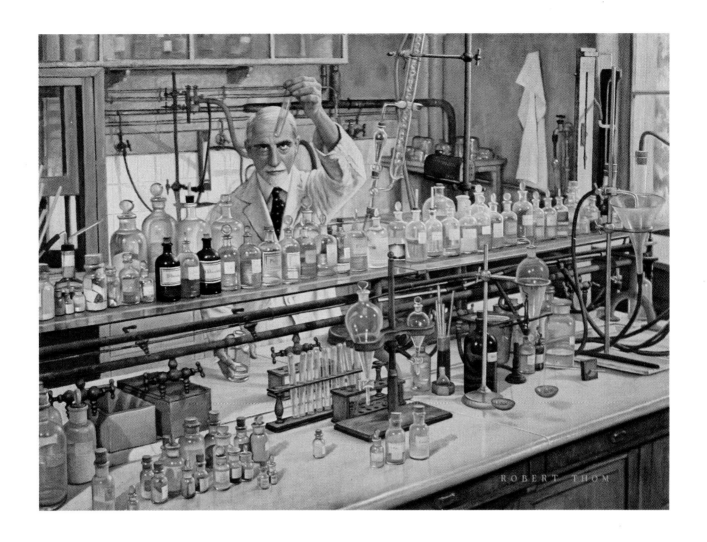

THE DEVELOPMENT OF CHEMOTHERAPY

One of the successful researchers in the development of new chemical compounds specifically created to fight disease-causing organisms in the body was the French pharmacist, Ernest François Auguste Fourneau (1872-1949), who for three decades headed chemical laboratories in the world-renowned Institut Pasteur, in Paris. His early work with bismuth and arsenic compounds advanced the treatment of syphilis. He broke the German secret of a specific for sleeping sickness; paved the way for the life-saving sulfonamide compounds; and from his laboratories came the first group of chemicals having recognized antihistaminic properties. His work led other investigators to broad fields of chemotherapeutic research.

181

Pharmacie in Paris, and in 1898, received his diploma as a *pharmacien*. He completed his training with three years of research in Germany under renowned leaders. In those days Germany was almost the sole world source of supply of synthetic drugs. "Fourneau," says T. A. Henry (*Journal of the Chemical Society*), "returned to France determined to do his utmost to bring his country to the front in this branch of the industry. He got the necessary opportunity in the research laboratories of Les Etablissements Poulenc Frères, of which he was made Director in 1903 and where he remained until 1911, when Dr. Roux offered him a post as principal of a laboratory of therapeutic chemistry at the Pasteur Institute (Paris), and in this congenial environment Fourneau passed the remainder of his working life." Henry then at length describes the highlights of Fourneau's work, but admirably sums up the unique qualities of this pharmacist-researcher as follows:

"In attempting an appreciation of Fourneau's work it must be remembered that he had a remarkable flair for envisaging the kind of molecular structure which would produce a particular pharmacologic effect, that for him chemistry was applicable to a wide range of therapeutics, and that he was gifted with a notable capacity for taking pains to bring his ideas to practical fruition."

Among Fourneau's early research projects was a study on amino alcohols and their derivatives with relation to the development of local anesthetic properties. Out of this came a product that was to become well known—stovaine. (He humorously linked the English term for his name [*fourneau*=stove] with this new compound.) His private laboratory at the Institut Pasteur remains today much the same as when Fourneau occupied it. It is now the laboratory of Mme. Trefouël, who succeeded to Fourneau's former post, and who is the wife of Jacques Trefouël, Directeur Actuel de l'Institut Pasteur, at present.

Although Fourneau made many contributions to the knowledge of therapeutically valuable chemical compounds early in the twentieth century, it was the world-electrifying announcement, in 1910, by the German physician-chemist Paul Ehrlich, and his Japanese collaborator, S. Hata, of their product, "606"—Salvarsan, or arsphenamine — as a specific against syphilis, that brought Fourneau to prominence.

"Shortly thereafter," says Urdang, "Fourneau, together with the Rumanian chemist, Constantin Levaditi, applied Ehrlich's ideas and methods to bismuth instead of arsenic, and created several bismuth compounds which paralleled and supplemented the arsphenamines.

"It was he who presented the world with acetarsone, the first effective arsenic compound that could be taken by mouth for use in prophylaxis and in treatment in certain cases of syphilis, as well as in the treatment of amebic dysentery. He called it stovarsol, again identifying a product with his name. What will perpetuate his name most, however, in the memory of the world at large, is the fact that he succeeded in discovering and in making available to everyone concerned the secret of two preparations which were intended to remain a German monopoly, not only for financial reasons but partly as a means of political pressure.

"It was due to the initiative and ingenuity of Fourneau that the secret specific against sleeping sickness, called by its German inventors (in the early 1920's) 'Bayer 205,' or 'Germanin,' and intended to be traded for political concessions with the nations interested in tropical colonies, was broken down and completely duplicated by a preparation called 'Fourneau 309.' It was likewise under the guidance and at the instigation of Fourneau that the secret of the German 'miracle drug,' prontosil, was revealed. By finding out that the remarkable effect of this drug was due to one distinct part of the complex molecule only, namely, to para-amino-benzene-sulfonamide, Fourneau and his collaborators, Constantin Levaditi and M. and Mme. Jacques Trefouël, paved the way for the chain of sulfonamide products which proved their life-saving capacity again and again. It was, furthermore, from the Fourneau laboratories at the Institut Pasteur that the first group of chemicals to earn the title of antihistaminic agents emanated.

"The notes in Poggendorff's biographical dictionary concerning Fourneau are, in fact, according to an editorial statement (*Eigene*

Mitteilung), autobiographical. In this autobiographical communication, designed to present himself to the world in the way he thought most adequate, Fourneau called himself first of all a *Pharmacien*. Only after thus having established his proper profession, he listed the various other distinctions and positions which he held.

"There is no doubt that Fourneau considered himself a *pharmacien* not merely because, in his youth, he met the requirements for a pharmaceutical diploma, but because he thought his entire life-work, devoted as it was to the improvement and enlargement of the drug armamentarium, to be pharmaceutical. In the opinion of Fourneau, pharmacy apparently is the sum total of all activities concerning drugs, be they distributive, industrial, or scientific; and his point of view is all the more authoritative as it was the result of his own successful experience in all these various activities."

In a memorial to Fourneau, published in the *Annales de l'Institut Pasteur*, the great pharmacist-chemist is referred to as the "successor to Ehrlich, the founder of chemotherapy." He did not lack appreciation in his lifetime—but many a person alive today has at some time had reason to give thanks to this pharmacist for the new disease-combating chemical compounds that got their start in the laboratory over which he presided.

WORLD EVENTS AND PHARMACY HISTORY

Dates, persons, and events of significance to the evolution of Pharmacy include:

1934	Santiago Ramón y Cajal died.
1934	György reported vitamin B_6 (pyridoxine).
1934	Joliot-Curie reported on artificial radiation and radioactive isotopes.
1934	Nobel prize awarded to Urey for discovering heavy hydrogen. Whipple, Minot, and Murphy awarded Nobel prize for discovery of liver treatment of anemia.
1935	Trefouel, Nitti, and Bovet (France) discovered prontosil's action to be due to sulfanilamide.
1935	Filatov improved corneal transplantation.
1935	Kendall and Reichstein isolated cortisone.
1935	Stanley discovered the virus agent of tobacco mosaic, a "living" molecule.
1935	Nucleic acids found to be principal components of viruses and genes.
1935	Witzleben developed the ultra-short-wave transmitter.
1935	Nobel prize awarded to Spemann for his studies in experimental embryology.
1935	H.W. Dudley isolated ergometrine.
1936	Bittner discovered agent of mammary tumor.
1936	Vitamin P announced.
1936	Nobel prize awarded to Dale and Loewi for their work on neurochemistry.
1936	Yeast hormone biotin (vitamin H) discovered by Kögl.
1937	Max Theiler developed yellow fever vaccine.
1937	Nicotinic acid announced.
1937	Sourdille improved fenestration operation.
1937	Sulfonamide therapy for gonorrhea.
1937	Nobel prizes awarded to Haworth and Karrer for their work in vitamin research, and to Szent-Györgyi for his discoveries in biological combustion.
1938	Harvey Cushing published *Meningiomas*.
1938	Vitamin E reported.
1938	Florey, Chain, and associates began work on penicillin.
1938	Dustin discovered the growth-stimulating effect of colchicine.

1938	Hess discovered the regulatory function of the midbrain.
1938	Hahn developed a device for nuclear fission.
1938	Carothers developed nylon.
1938	Heinkel adapted the turbine engine for use in aviation.
1938	Nobel prizes awarded to Kuhn for vitamin research and to Heymans for his discovery of the vascular regulation of respiration.
1939	Harvey Williams Cushing died.
1939	R. J. Dubos described tyrothricin.
1939	R. E. Gross operated on open ductus arteriosus.
1939	World War II began, Sept. 1. (Many advances in the treatment of wounds and traumatic infections, sanitation methods, and improvements in prosthetic limbs.)
1939	P. Muller (Switzerland) introduced DDT insecticide.
1939	Florey and Chain (England) developed penicillin to stage of therapeutic use.
1939	More than 150 different kinds of synthetic materials known.
1939	Gibbons developed blood circulation apparatus, "artificial heart."
1939	Nobel prizes awarded to Domagk for his discovery of the antibacterial action of prontosil, and to Butenandt for his work on sex hormones.
1940	Florey, Chain, and associates published work on penicillin as chemotherapeutic agent.
1940	Pantothenic acid synthesized.
1940	Inositol proved essential vitamin by Woolley.
1940	Karl Link (U.S.) discovered dicumarol.
1940	Landsteiner and Wiener discovered the Rhesus factor in blood.
1940	Development of plastic facial surgery.
1940	Euthanasia practiced in Germany.
1941	Frederick G. Banting died.
1941	Charles Huggins (U.S.) arrested prostatic cancer with female hormone.
1941	U.S.A. entered World War II after Japanese attack on Pearl Harbor.
1941	Sinizin transplanted a second heart.

PHARMACEUTICAL RESEARCH

RESEARCH in some form has gone hand in hand with the development of Pharmacy through the ages. The ancients, Shen Nung (2600 B.C.), Theophrastus, Galen, and Dioscorides, and countless of their contemporaries, conducted research of a sort, based almost entirely on keen observation and trial-and-error experimentation. Even though Paracelsus, in the first half of the sixteenth century, advocated that only pure substances should be employed in medicine, realization of this ideal could come only when chemistry, especially organic chemistry, had reached a high level of development. Says **Dr. K. Miescher**, in his paper, *Drugs in the Advance of Science:* "The manufacture of medicaments on the basis of exact, and above all, systematic research into their effects, is of very recent origin. It had to await the opening up of wide fields of science, such as chemistry and physics . . .

"The history of the natural sciences and medicine is part and parcel of the general development of Western thought. Certain well-established stages marked this development: the Greeks' efforts to penetrate nature's secrets by the processes of reasoning; the first steps in pharmaceutical chemistry as attempted by pharmacists of Paracelsus' time; the decisive turn toward systematization of natural sciences on a mathematical basis during the Renaissance; and the beginning of modern chemistry about 1790, as originated by Lavoisier. While the cradle of chemistry still rested in the pharmacy during the eighteenth and even part of the nineteenth century, independent chemical laboratories began to appear, under the stimulation of Liebig's pioneer efforts.

"Chemistry had at last reached the stage at which a significant development in pharmacy was possible. Even so, the fruits of this

PHARMACEUTICAL RESEARCH

Research in some form has gone hand in hand with the development of Pharmacy through the ages. However, it was the chemical synthesis of antipyrine in 1883 that gave impetus and inspiration for intensive search for therapeutically useful compounds. Begun by the Germans, who dominated the field until World War I, the lead in pharmaceutical research passed thereafter to the United States. Research in Pharmacy came into its own in the late 1930's and early 1940's; has grown steadily since, due to the support of pharmaceutical manufacturers, universities, and government. Today it uses techniques and trained personnel from every branch of science in the unending search for new life-saving and life-giving drug products.

advance were slow to ripen during the course of the last century.

"Until far into the second half of the nineteenth century, investigators were concerned mainly with the isolation of pure, active substances from known drugs. This was followed very much later by the establishment of their molecular composition, the elucidation of their chemical constitution, and their synthesis from simple substances. Finally, it was even possible to create altogether new medicaments . . ."

Another view of the development of pharmaceutical research is expressed by Dr. Ivor Griffith, in a paper entitled, *Medicines in the Making:*

"Many believe that research was born in Germany, but this is not strictly true. Research, like Topsy, just grew. Yet it is significant that Germany, in the chemical field, was very much the foster mother to research, for that country did endow research with a momentum that made for substantial progress.

"After the young Englishman Perkin discovered the aniline dye, mauve, Britain neglected to follow his lead to greater discoveries in the same direction. Germany, however, saw the possibilities and allocated huge sums of government money to finance scientific research, at first mainly in the synthetic dye field. Creative chemistry grew, under the German system, until extensive advances had been made, not only in dyestuffs but also in medicinal chemicals, explosives, and metallurgic factors. This surge of progress continued until World War I interrupted the program." The lead in pharmaceutical research passed eventually to the United States.

In a summary of the highlights of progress of research in the field of pharmaceuticals, Dr. Miescher comments that: "It is not surprising that the first results were obtained in the field of alkaloids, these being nitrogen-containing bases that could be readily extracted from the herbal drugs with dilute acids . . . This group is headed by morphine, discovered by Sertürner in the early years of the nineteenth century and generally recognized in 1817. It took a long time to establish chemical constitution and to achieve the first synthesis. Not until 1884, fifty-seven years after its discovery, was coniine, the simplest of the alkaloids, recognized as *a*-n-propylpiperidine; its synthesis was effected two years later . . . Nearly 1,000 alkaloids are known today.

"The development of organic chemistry and the rise of pharmacology at the end of the nineteenth century made it possible to tackle the problem of producing synthetic medicaments not patterned on substances occurring in nature . . . The first successes were achieved in the field of antipyretics and analgesics . . ." But the chemists frequently knew not what they had created. Salicylic acid, aspirin, and acetanilid, for example, were known long before the discovery of their specific medicinal effects.

Dr. George Urdang quotes Bockmuhl as saying, "It is hardly possible to imagine to what extent the discovery of antipyrine excited not only the chemists but the physicians also." Dr. Urdang adds the further comment: "It was not so much that antipyrine proved to be such an effective antipyretic. The fact that it could be used as a basis for further research meant much more. Although aspirin, brought on the market in 1898 at the instigation of Bichengrun, was much more effective than antipyrine, it did not offer the theoretical interest aroused by antipyrine."

Dr. Griffith further observes: "Of all the industries, the drug industry was the first to realize that organized, systematized research had to be fostered and well financed . . . Long before the textile trades, the metallurgical industries, and many other key industries in our present day civilization had thought of conducting a bold program of research, manufacturing pharmacy had done so . . . It is on record that Parke, Davis & Company of Detroit, Michigan, had a research department, and an active one, operating on its own budget as far back as about 1880. Today, no large manufacturing house is without a research division dedicated to both pure and applied research."

In 1902, Parke, Davis & Company completed what is believed to be the first building in the United States, if not in the world, a major portion of which was devoted to pharmaceutical research. This laboratory, on the banks of the Detroit River, and the expanded facilities which have developed since, have been the birthplace of many sound and sometimes spectacular advances in the fields of Pharmacy and Medicine.

Pharmaceutical research in the United States followed a fairly definite periodic pattern of progression. The earliest was the formative period, in the mid-1800's, when investigations carried on in retail pharmacies began to demand larger quarters, and the transition to small pharmaceutical manufacturing plants began. The second phase, stemming directly from the first, was that of botanical research, beginning about 1875, during which explorations were conducted searching for new plants possessing medicinal properties, and methods developed for extracting the active principles. Next came the standardization period, beginning about 1882, when attention was given to methods of extraction and assay that would provide uniform strengths and potencies in each lot of pharmaceutical preparations. The biological period got under way in 1895. Research and developments in this field provided a quiet but remarkable revolution in Medicine. The chemotherapeutic age was initiated also in the late 1890's; and the antibiotics came to the fore in the early 1940's, as a result of many years of intermittent research advances.

Though the entry of each of these new fields of research into the pharmaceutical picture has affected both Pharmacy and Medicine profoundly, and each in turn has led to the development of new medicinal agents which to a considerable degree have affected or supplanted the use of the products of earlier areas of research, each of these broad fields still continues to contribute valuable and important developments to modern medical practice. For example, in the middle 1950's, the botanists and the chemists uncovered rauwolfia's long-hidden hypotensive and tranquilizing benefits. Every medicinal product, from whatever source, is now subjected to rigid standards and tests for quality, strength and purity. Biological researchers have contributed a vaccine against poliomyelitis, and are following many other important leads. Chemotherapeutic research has contributed countless new products, not the least of which are the antihistamines and the tranquilizers. Research in the antibiotic field has provided drugs which control many infections that formerly brought dread to the hearts of both patient and physician.

No one broad field of pharmaceutical research, therefore, has either completely supplanted the other or become obsolete, despite the revolutionary changes in the middle of the twentieth century.

Research in the pharmaceutical field really came into its own in the late 1930's and early 1940's, stimulated by the demands of World War II. It has continued to grow steadily since, and to turn out an increasing array of products for clinical evaluation; for development under modern mass production; for prescription by physicians; and for distribution, on a world-wide basis, as close by as the community pharmacy. This phenomenal growth of research has resulted from the financial support accorded it by pharmaceutical manufacturers, universities, and governments. The public has benefited beyond measure—and millions of people owe their lives to the advances made against disease within the walls of these laboratories.

Another marked change took place in pharmaceutical research during the second quarter of the twentieth century. The methods of doing research gradually changed from an individual effort to a team basis. More and more brilliant discoveries resulted, not from the efforts of a single scientist, but usually from well-coordinated teamwork by groups of scientists, each a specialist in his own field. The trained personnel from every branch of science bring to bear their specialized knowledge and techniques in the search for new life-saving and life-giving drug products. It is to the dedicated efforts of people such as these in countless laboratories that mankind owes a debt of gratitude for the advantages which modern Pharmacy and Medicine are enabled to provide.

Despite these tremendous advances in the field of pharmaceutical research, says Dr. Miescher, "We are undoubtedly only at the beginning of an extremely fruitful period . . . We all know that great therapeutic problems are waiting for solution . . ."

A most fitting conclusion is to be found in the words of Dr. Griffith:

"Those who think of evolution as progress frequently forget that the projecting curve carries on into the long tomorrows, and perhaps with an acceleration of its pace. Could we sit a hundred years hence and think of meantime progress of research and achievement in the healing arts, we would more than likely be stunned by its results and by its pace. And will the world of tomorrow be a better world to live in? The pharmacists of today are doing what they can to try to make it so."

WORLD EVENTS AND PHARMACY HISTORY

Dates, persons, and events of significance to the evolution of Pharmacy include:

1942   Collection of blood donations begun by Red Cross in U.S.A. for treating battle casualties. Forerunner of blood bank system.

1942   Atomic energy released and controlled in first nuclear chain reaction.

1942   First jet aircraft tested at Muroc, California.

1942   Opening of Alcan Highway.

1942   Food and gasoline rationing in U.S.

1943   Penicillin production gets under way.

1943   Selman A. Waksman announced discovery of streptomycin.

1943   Cell smear method used to detect uterine cancer.

1943   ACTH isolated from the anterior pituitary gland.

1943   Nobel prize awarded to Dam and Doisy for their research on vitamin K.

1944   First operation for asphyxia livida.

1944   Synthesis of quinine.

1944   Negorski performed first resuscitation following clinical death.

1944   Nobel prize awarded to Erlanger and Gasser for their discoveries in neurologic research.

1945   Promin® (sodium glucosulfone) effective against leprosy, made available by Parke-Davis.

1945   Walter Bradford Cannon died.

1945   Fleming, Florey, and Chain jointly awarded Nobel prize.

1945   Alfred Blalock, Helen Taussig, (U.S.) devised "blue baby" operation.

1945   First atomic bomb explosion.

1945   End of World War II, April 6.

1945   World-wide antimalarial campaign with DDT.

1945   First session of the U.N.

1946   Thiamin and folic acid used in treatment for pernicious anemia.

1946   Nobel prize awarded to H. J. Müller for his research on x-ray mutations.

1946   Paris conference clash between U. S. and U.S.S.R. marks beginning of "cold war."

1946   Penicillin produced synthetically.

1947   Parke-Davis research team announced discovery of Chloromycetin® (chloramphenicol).

1947   Rocket aircraft (Bell X-1) developed in U.S.A. with speeds up to 1500 m.p.h.

1947   Nobel prizes awarded to C. Cori, G. Cori, and B. Houssay for their studies on metabolism of glycogen and sugar.

1948   B. M. Duggar (Lederle) announced discovery of aureomycin.

1948   Rickes and Smith described vitamin B_{12} (cyanocobalamin).

1948   Sidney Farber found antagonists to folic acid alleviate leukemia.

1948   Charles Bailey (U.S.) improved heart surgery.

1948   World Health Organization founded.

1948   Kinsey report on *Sexual Behavior of the Human Male.*

1948   200-inch telescope installed in Mount Palomar Observatory.

1948   Therapeutic properties of cortisone recognized.

1948   Berlin Air Lift.

1948   Nobel prize awarded to Müller for his discovery of DDT.

1949   Betatron used in cancer therapy.

1949   Two-stage rocket (250 miles high).

1949   North Atlantic Treaty Organization founded in Washington, D.C.

1949   Dedication of permanent U.N. site in New York City.

1949   Nobel prize awarded to Hess and Moniz for their studies on physiology and surgery of the brain.

1950   Team of Pfizer researchers announced discovery of terramycin.

1950   Beginning of Korean conflict.

1950   Intensified interest in geriatric medicine due to longer life expectancy.

1950   A.M.A. launched vigorous program opposing socialized medicine.

1950   Müller developed the electron field microscope.

1950   Nobel prize awarded to Hench, Kendall and Reichstein for their studies on treatment of rheumatoid arthritis with cortisone and ACTH.

1951   Ludwig Gross showed virus transmission of leukemia in mice.

1951   André-Thomas developed the heart-lung machine.

1951   Operation with vegetative blockade by Laborit.

1951   International Pharmacopoeia of the World Health Organization.

PHARMACEUTICAL MANUFACTURING COMES OF AGE

PHARMACEUTICAL manufacturing, as an industry apart from its parent, retail Pharmacy, had its beginning about 1600 A.D. It got under way in the middle 1700's. It was stimulated in 1918 by World War I, but really "came of age" in the early 1940's, at the beginning of World War II, when necessity, in the form of lack of manpower and machinery, demanded the use of ingenuity to create new methods and tools; and gave impetus to the invention of ways to increase the volume of manufacturing production by tenfold and hundredfold per man and machine.

The "prescriptions" or formulas filled by the manufacturing branch of Pharmacy consist of tons and tank-car quantities, as compared to the dozen capsules or four-ounce mixtures compounded in the dispensary of the retail pharmacy.

Large-scale (relatively speaking) production of certain drugs preceded by many centuries this period of recognizable separation of the retail and manufacturing phases of Pharmacy. It existed in the time of Greek and Roman antiquity and in the Middle Ages. As Dr. Urdang points out: "The production of *terra sigillata* (sealed earth) tablets, begun in the fifth century B.C., and so highly praised by Galen, consisting of the special greasy clay found on the island of Lemnos, were sold over the entire known world up to the late Middle Ages. There was large-scale manufacture of

PHARMACEUTICAL MANUFACTURING COMES OF AGE

Pharmaceutical manufacturing as an industry apart from retail Pharmacy had its beginnings about 1600; really got under way in the middle 1700's. It developed first in Germany, then in England and in France. In America, it was the child of wars—born during the Revolution; grew rapidly during and following the Civil War; became independent of Europe during World War I; came of age during and following World War II. Utilizing latest technical advances from every branch of science, manufacturing Pharmacy economically develops and produces the latest and greatest drugs in immense quantities, so that everywhere physicians may prescribe them and pharmacists dispense them for the benefit of all mankind.

distilled waters and perfumes in the thirteenth century and later in some monasteries in Italy, France and Germany, and of the Venetian troches of vipers in Venice. However, these early precursors of pharmaceutical mass production were almost exclusively caused by the accident of the presence of local raw material granting a practical monopoly to the producers . . . The large-scale production of earlier times was essentially incidental and conservative. Modern industrial mass production has been systematically planned and progressive."

In another analysis of the subject, "Retail Pharmacy as the Nucleus of the Pharmaceutical Industry," published in the *Bulletin of the History of Medicine*, Dr. Urdang offers further interesting observations and data. In this, he states:

"It was about two hundred years ago, in the middle of the eighteenth century, that the beginnings of a pharmaceutical industry replacing the traditional small scale manufacturing by the retail pharmacists became obvious. Thus when about another fifty years later, in the early nineteenth century, the general conditions in the world at large offered an opportunity not only to a few industries favored by special circumstances, or to a few industrialists gifted with special scientific or organizational talents, the new development found in pharmacy a well prepared soil.

"The fact that retail pharmacy sheltered and cultivated the young science of chemistry in the eighteenth and early nineteenth centuries made the pharmaceutical retail stores and their laboratories in the countries concerned the birthplace not only of the pharmaceutical industry but also of a great part of applied technical chemistry. This scientific development took place in England, France and Germany. In the United States of America the pharmaceutical industry developed somewhat later on a different basis. Here too, however, it was retail pharmacy that took part in the start as well as the growth of this industry to an amazing extent.

"About 1660 the great English chemist Robert Boyle brought a young German, Ambrosius Gottfried Hanckwitz, to London and established for his protégé a chemist's shop with a spacious laboratory. The latter, about 1700, developed into a pharmaceutical manufacturing plant of international renown." Hanckwitz later took the name of Godfrey, and according to his advertising bills, he prepared faithfully all sorts of remedies, chemical and galenical.

"A genuine pharmacist," continues Urdang, "who was registered not only in the list of Parisian *Maîtres d'Apothicaires* (1752) but also in the long and proud roster of famous scientists of pharmaceutical origin, was the Frenchman, Antoine Baumé (1728-1804). It is he whom we rightly may consider as the first retail druggist making the laboratory of his store the starting point of an important manufacturing plant on the basis of scientific knowledge and technical skill . . . He introduced the hydrometer, and 'Baumé's degrees' still bear his name . . . He improved the process of distillation and gave in 1757 the first definite formula for the preparation of ether . . . In 1775, Baumé issued a price list of pharmaceutical and chemical preparations. This list of 88 pages contains about 2400 individual items . . . Baumé established the first factory for the manufacture of ammonium chloride."

From this point on the number of pharmacists enlarging the laboratories of their stores to factories grew in proportion with the eminent part played by French and German pharmacists in the development of science.

The extraordinary attention paid to the alkaloids in the early part of the nineteenth century had a practical as well as a theoretical value. The practical value of these new substances lay in their undeniable efficiency as medicinal agents. Their theoretical importance, however, was of even greater bearing. Purity now became the goal of Pharmacy and the pharmaceutical manufacturing industry.

In contrast to France and Germany, according to Urdang, the part played by the English retail pharmacists in the development of modern chemistry was not so aggressive. "As a matter of fact," he says, "there was about 1800 in England no really consolidated profession of pharmacy. There were apothecaries with predominantly medical ambitions, who regarded pharmacy merely as a subordinate menial activity. There were chemists on the one hand

Early Pharmaceutical Manufacturing Firms

A list, admittedly incomplete, of British, German and French pharmaceutical establishments that had their beginnings in retail pharmacies and grew to significance in manufacturing pharmacy, includes the following:

1660	Robert Boyle[1]—England
1741	Burgoyne, Burbidges & Co., Ltd.—England
1752	Antoine Baumé—France
1780	J. F. Macfarlan & Company—Scotland
1780	Savory and Moore, Ltd.—England
1790	Wright, Layman & Umney, Ltd.—England
1795	Allen and Hanburys, Ltd.—England
1798	John Bell & Croyden—England
1807	Howard and Sons[2]—England
1814	Daken Brothers, Ltd.—England
1814	J. D. Riedel[3]—Germany
1817	Friedrich Wilhelm Sertürner—Germany
1820	Joseph Pelletier and J. B. Caventou—France
1821	Thomas Morson and Son—England
1827	H. E. Merck[4]—Germany
1831	Squire & Sons, Ltd.—England
1833	Stafford, Allen & Sons, Ltd.—England
1834	May & Baker, Ltd.—England
1837	Hermann Trommsdorff[5]—Germany
1851	Ernst Schering—Germany
1856	Friedrich Witte—Germany
1880	Stanislas Limousin—France
1880	Burroughs, Wellcome & Company[6]—England

[1]Succeeded by A. Gottfried Hanckwitz, who later changed his name to Godfrey.

[2]Allen and Hanburys, Ltd., London, and Howard and Sons, Ltd., Ilford, were both offspring of the same retail drug store, the Plough Court Pharmacy of London, established by Silvanus Bevan in 1715.

[3]Riedel was a student of the great apothecary chemist, M. H. Klaproth, who is credited with the discovery of uranium.

[4]H. E. Merck's manufacturing activities, begun in 1827, grew out of the family pharmacy at Darmstadt, which was established in 1688.

[5]Actually, Hermann Trommsdorff revived a pharmaceutical operation begun many years earlier by his famous scientist grandfather, Joh. Bartholomaeus Trommsdorff.

[6]Though significant among English manufacturing firms, Burroughs, Wellcome & Company does not rightly belong in a list of pharmaceutical manufacturers having developed from retail pharmacies. Both Silas M. Burroughs and Henry S. Wellcome were graduates of the Philadelphia College of Pharmacy. Both were employed by John Wyeth and Brother, Inc., of Philadelphia, Pennsylvania, before founding the firm in London in 1880. Though having had retail experience, neither partner had ever owned an apothecary shop.

and druggists on the other, and only a very few people who could be regarded as professional pharmacists. Nevertheless, it was these few who laid the groundwork for the modern English pharmaceutical industry. Their early production was based not as much upon scientific discoveries of their own as upon the realization of the business possibilities involved . . .

"It is significant that many of the (English) retail druggists who developed into industrialists were instrumental in the revival of English professional pharmacy. William Allen and Daniel Bell Hanbury of Allen and Hanburys, Thomas Morson of Thomas Morson and Son, John May of May and Baker, John Savory of Savory and Moore, and Peter Squire of Squire and Sons, belonged to the small group of ambitious and courageous English pharmacists who, in 1841, founded the Pharmaceutical Society of Great Britain that in the course of time became the officially recognized self-governing body of English Pharmacy."

The development of manufacturing Pharmacy in the United States, Urdang calls "the child of wars." Elaborating on this, he says: "It was born during the Revolutionary War (1775-1783). It took the decisive step from childhood to manhood after and in consequence of the Civil War (1861-1865); and it became independent from Europe and dominant in the world market after World War I (1914-1918). World War II (1941-1945) made this dominance a generally accepted fact."

Elaborating on the beginning of pharmaceutical manufacture in the New World, Urdang points out that "The North American colonies were, naturally, not able to develop a pharmaceutico-chemical industry of their own. The country was thinly settled, the means of transportation poor, and finally and decisively it was not in the interest of the mother country England to promote or even permit an industrial development apt to diminish the English export to the colonies. Thus it was not until the end of the Revolutionary War that large scale production of pharmaceutical chemicals was started (in the United States). The firm of Christopher, Jr., and Charles Marshall, retail and wholesale druggists in Philadelphia, in 1786, entered into the commercial production of ammonium chloride and Glauber's salt. It is of interest that the first people to produce ammonium chloride commercially in Europe, as well as on American soil, the Parisian apothecary Beaumé and the Philadelphia druggists Marshall, were retail pharmacists . . .

"That pharmaceutical industry which grew up from American retail pharmacy was in its beginning mainly based on galenical preparations. In 1838 the Philadelphia retail druggist, Robert Shoemaker, successfully developed a process for making plasters other than by hand and became a large scale manufacturer of this article. The same man is said to have been the first (in the United States) to prepare glycerin commercially, probably according to the method made known by the most famous retail pharmacist of all time, Scheele, who recognized glycerin in 1783.

"The utilization of indigenous drugs played an important part in the development of the American pharmaceutical industry . . . The process of percolation, invented in France, but owing its development mainly to American retail pharmacists, became the domain and the starting point of manufacturing on a large scale . . . It was on the same basis that they (pharmacists in the United States) developed a new industry by inventing new processes and improving old ones for the preparation of products hitherto manufactured in a rather primitive way and with primitive results . . ."

In a very interesting article entitled "Forty-five years of Manufacturing Pharmacy," read before the Historical Section of the American Pharmaceutical Association at its sixty-second annual convention at Detroit in 1914, Dr. Frank O. Taylor states that:

"Up to the time of the early 'sixties (1860's) it had been the almost universal custom for each pharmacist to prepare for himself such galenical preparations as he needed, but about this time several firms began manufacturing work on a small scale, developing this in most cases in retail drug stores that had been established for some years. The idea of centralized manufacture of medicinal preparations was just in its infancy and was probably not recognized as such at that time . . ." He then described the events which led to the beginning of Parke, Davis & Company in 1866. Dr. Taylor then observes that:

"The history of Manufacturing Pharmacy as a whole and of Parke, Davis & Company may be divided into four periods characterized by the most important activity of the time, which periods are practically identical in date, especially the last three, as this firm in each of these was the leader in the special work involved. These periods are as follows:

1. Formative Period—1867 to 1874.
2. Botanical Research Period—1875 to 1882.
3. Standardization Period—1882 to 1894.
4. Biological Period—1895 to present time.

"These are of course not sharply defined; the work characteristic of each of the last three was in the course of development for some time before the dates assigned, and the appearance of a new line of work by no means indicated a termination of previous endeavors . . ."

To Dr. Taylor's classifications stated in 1914, must be added further specific classifications—

5. Organic Chemical Synthesis, beginning 1883.
6. Hormones, beginning 1901.
7. Vitamins, beginning 1909.
8. Antibiotics, beginning 1940.

"Until World War I," states Urdang, "most of the products of the German pharmaceutico-chemical industry were only sold, not manufactured, in the United States, being protected from imitation by American patents . . ."

In its issue of January, 1955, *Drug and Cosmetic Industry* published a list of 31 oldest drug houses in the United States. This statement preceded the list: "In our December, 1949, issue we published a list of the 'eight oldest drug houses' which appeared in the Reed & Carnrick *Quarterly*. Upon publication of this list we were informed of other houses that belonged in it. We arbitrarily decided to end the list with Eli Lilly, which was the last house to be named in the original one, and thus the last year appearing on the list is 1876 . . ."

31 Oldest Drug Houses

Caswell-Massey Co., Ltd. 1752
Schieffelin & Company 1781
Lanman & Kemp-Barclay & Co. 1808
The Tilden Company 1824
S.S.S. Company 1826
The Wm. S. Merrell Company 1828
McKesson & Robbins 1833
Strong Cobb & Co. 1833
Boericke & Tafel 1835
Otis Clapp & Son 1840
Smith, Kline & French 1841
Carroll Dunham Smith Pharmacal Co. .1844
Sharp & Dohme 1845
Solon Palmer 1847
Chicago Pharmacal Company 1855
Hance Bros. & White Co. 1855
William R. Warner & Co.* 1856
E. R. Squibb & Sons 1858
Reed & Carnrick 1860
Wyeth, Inc. 1860
The Burrough Bros. Mfg. Co. 1863
Buffington's 1865
Parke, Davis & Company 1866
Borcherdt Malt Extract Company 1868
Lloyd Brothers, Inc. 1870
Valentine Company 1871
Henry K. Wampole & Co. 1872
Chilcott Laboratories* 1875
Lydia E. Pinkham Medicine Company .1875
The Arlington Chemical Company 1876
Eli Lilly & Company 1876

*Now merged.

"The most important manufacturing advance," noted Dr. Taylor in his 1914 paper, "has been the development of new machinery, so that where originally a few tablets might be made by the retail druggist by hand and later by a machine giving a single tablet at each impression, we now have especially designed machinery which has a capacity of a million and a half tablets per ten-hour day . . ."

Many of the mechanical improvements in manufacturing pharmacy came from the ideas and inventions, most mothered by necessity, of the men who were charged with the operation of the machines. Thus there grew up not only a corps of chemical engineers, but also a class of pharmaceutical engineers, highly versatile and capable of performing near miracles of production from the equipment they designed. In the 1890's, for example, it was visualized that manufacture of empty gelatin capsules might someday reach the staggering production peak of one million capsules a year. Sixty years later, production of one million capsules would have occupied hardly more than an hour's time in a well-ordered division of a pharmaceutical manufacturing plant.

The vastly stepped-up demands of World War II for all types of pharmaceuticals, plus the concurrent shortages of steel and other metals on the one hand, and of manpower on the other, placed an unprecedented strain and pressure on pharmaceutical manufacturing facilities. Almost overnight, manufacturing administrators were faced with the multiple problems of stepping up production of existing machinery a hundredfold or a thousandfold; of accomplishing this increase with diminished manpower; and of keeping existing machinery, strained beyond all intended capacity, in shape for 'round-the-clock operation. The fact that the pharmaceutical industry met this unprecedented challenge is at once a tribute to management and employees; and an accomplishment to which countless millions of persons, both civilians and fighting personnel, owe their lives.

The story of penicillin and other antibiotics, developed within a few years from a laboratory curiosity made in small flasks to high-tonnage production in 5- to 50,000-gallon tanks, is but one of the near-miraculous accomplishments of the turbulent '40's and early '50's of the twentieth century.

"It is significant," says Urdang, "that most of the large drug manufacturing plants in the United States have established footholds, subsidiaries and branches in other countries, not only in

North and South America, Europe, and Australia, but in South Africa and the Near and Far East, as well. The United States, a country which once imported scientific ideas as well as most of the products based on them, has become an exporter of both."

The 200-year development of the pharmaceutical industry from its parent, the retail pharmacy, was not accomplished without many misgivings and much opposition on the part of the body pharmaceutic, however. Though most manufacturing plants stemmed from their midst, many retail pharmacists were loud in their protests against what they considered to be an encroachment upon their pride and prerogatives. Many attempts were made and much discussion and propaganda disseminated in resistance to the trend toward more and more production of drugs and medicinal preparations in central manufacturing plants. However, in time the problems attendant with standardization, biological products, complex chemical synthesis, and popularization of parenteral medication proved too much for the greater number of retail outlets. Added to this, the public acceptance of the more elegant products of mass production, plus the ease and convenience of dispensing, won over all but the most individualistic pharmacists in retailing. It remained a popular tradition among retail pharmacists for many decades, however, when in casual conversation, to refer to their manufacturing brethren with a standard and somewhat impious two-word prefix.

Reviewing this situation, Urdang observes that "Doubtless industry has taken over almost completely the manufacturing earlier executed by retail pharmacy. As far as galenicals are concerned, retail pharmacy and not industry has to be blamed. As a matter of fact, the opinion that industry has robbed retail pharmacy of its manufacturing activities is wrong because the latter partly left it voluntarily to industry, and because, and this is even more important, the industrial products very often represent new creations or specialties, the preparation of which is not within the means of the average retail pharmacy.

"The fact that in spite of the extraordinary development of industrial production of pharmaceuticals, retail pharmacy during this period has not decreased but increased in volume as well as in importance in all countries of the civilized world, is an economic phenomenon. It can be explained only by two other facts. First, the pharmaceutical industry has created new needs to the advantage of retail pharmacy. Second, retail pharmacy has proved to be indispensable and irreplaceable as the fitting and distributing agency of the products concerned. There is a limit to mechanizing and schematizing in medicine and in pharmacy. Between the individual physician and the individual patient, the individual pharmacist cannot be missed . . . Each efficient remedy strengthens the confidence of the public in remedial therapy in general, and in the distributing agency, the retail pharmacy, in particular.

"Manufacturing and retail pharmacy are two branches of the same tree."

THE ERA OF ANTIBIOTICS

THE FULL revolutionary impact of the discovery and development of antibiotics upon the twin professions of Pharmacy and Medicine cannot yet be measured. Its profound significance can be grasped only in the perspective of the tragico-ironic likelihood that the microbial sources of these lifesaving drugs have been present in the good earth as long as man has lived upon it. Only in the second quarter of the twentieth century did man's powers of observation and scientific understanding develop to the point where he could recognize the potentials of antibiotic phenomena and direct them to his advantage. This marked a new and dramatic departure from previously established pharmaceutical and therapeutic strategy in attacking disease.

The concept and development of antibiotic substances as therapeutic agents resulted from a chain of events that got under way in the middle of the nineteenth century. At that time, people in central Europe, central Asia, and elsewhere, were deliberately growing molds, probably types of *Penicillium*, for the purpose of applying them to infected wounds. In 1877, the French chemist Louis Pasteur and his colleague, J. Joubert, demonstrated antibiotic action against a disease-producing germ. They observed that anthrax bacilli growing in urine were destroyed if the urine was also sown with some "common bacteria." This observation

THE ERA OF ANTIBIOTICS

Antibiotics are not new. Their actions probably were first observed by Pasteur in 1877. However, the second quarter of the 20th century marked the flowering of the antibiotic era—a new and dramatic departure in the production of disease-fighting drugs. Fleming's discovery of penicillin in 1929 went undeveloped until Florey and Chain studied it in 1940. Under pressure of World War II, pharmaceutical manufacturers rapidly adapted mass production methods to penicillin; have reduced its cost to 1/1000th the original. Antibiotic discoveries came rapidly in the '40's. Intensive research continues to find antibiotics that will conquer more of man's microbial enemies.

and later ones, they pointed out prophetically, "perhaps justify the highest hopes for therapeutics." This was the first scientifically recorded observation of the activity which has come to be termed "antibiosis."

Pasteur's major interest lay in the field of immunity, and he pursued his observation of the antibiotic phenomenon no further. In the years that followed, however, many scientists reported observations or investigations involving antagonism between organisms.

A. V. Cornil and V. Babes wrote in a French medical journal in 1885 that "If the study of mutual antagonisms of bacteria was sufficiently far advanced, a disease caused by one bacterium could probably be treated by another . . ."

The German scientist K. G. Doehle is said to have offered, in 1889, the first actual illustration of antibiotic action: diffusion of an antibiotic from a colony of *Micrococcus anthracotoxicus*, to form a sterile zone in an agar plate of anthrax bacilli.

In 1896, an Italian scientist, B. Gosio, discovered the first antibiotic produced by a mold of the genus *Penicillium*, now called mycophenolic acid, which inhibited anthrax bacilli. The following year a French scientist, E. Duchesne, reported that "certain green *Penicillia* are capable of repressing the growth of various bacteria or of bringing about their attenuation."

Another pioneer who carried forward the search for antibiotics was the Belgian scientist, A. Gratia. For sixteen years, 1923 to 1939, he and his collaborators studied the problem. They discovered "Gratia's substance" (later called actinomycetin) and, according to Florey, undoubtedly used it clinically, long before penicillin was so used, "not only for immunization purposes but for real therapeutic purposes."

Prior to the introduction of penicillin, the work of Dubos in the United States had resulted in the introduction of gramicidin, tyrocidine, and tyrothricin. Toxicity prevented their use internally, and their value was confined to local application.

Despite the half century of investigations that preceded it, there is no question that the discovery of penicillin in 1928 by Professor

208

Alexander Fleming of St. Mary's Hospital in London was the trigger that set off the chain reaction of research and production activities that ushered in the modern antibiotic era. However, as John F. Fulton has discerningly pointed out, "We are driven inescapably to the conclusion that credit for the introduction of penicillin as a therapeutic agent does not go to Pasteur, nor Gratia, nor Fleming, nor to the many others . . . but rather to those who first isolated penicillin and gave clearcut proof of its clinical usefulness, its assay and dosage, as well as the mode of its excretion from the body."

Much has been made, both in fact and fiction, of Fleming's "accidental" discovery of penicillin. Accidental contamination of one microbial culture by another has been a frequent occurrence since the beginning of mycological and bacteriological study. Such accidents assume significance only when the combination of a natural phenomenon and its observation by a trained scientific mind leads to some new avenue of thought and study.

Professor Fleming, Fulton reports, accidentally allowed several of his petri dishes on which staphylococci were growing to remain uncovered before an open window, one day in 1928. The next day, he found that they had been contaminated by an airborne fungus, later identified as the mold *Penicillium notatum*. He observed that wherever the mold had begun to grow, the bacterial colonies had either stopped growing or disappeared. Instead of casting the contaminated cultures aside, he made note of the growth inhibition, finding that it extended for some distance beyond the actual growth of the mold. From this, according to his report in 1929, Fleming concluded that the mold must give forth a chemical substance which diffuses for some distance into the culture medium. Realizing that there might be therapeutic possibilities if the agent which had inhibited the bacteria could be extracted from the mold, Fleming set about to grow the mold in broth and to make extracts of the broth in the hope of capturing the active growth-inhibiting principle. In the course of his studies he found that whatever was elaborated by the *Penicillium* mold served to inhibit most of the gram-positive pathogenic organisms, which included streptococcus, staphylococcus, meningococcus, and the gram-negative gonococcus. He also observed that soil organisms, interestingly enough, were resistant to the growth-inhibiting agent of the *Penicillium* mold.

Believing that the growth-inhibiting effects were due to a specific agent in the mold, Fleming, finding the phrase "mold broth filtrate" cumbersome, named it "penicillin." He and his associates, Clutterbuck, Lovell, and Raistrick, at the London School of Hygiene and Tropical Medicine, attempted to extract the penicillin, but without much success. They did determine, however, that it was destroyed by heat, and was relatively nontoxic to animals. Here the subject was left, and Fleming made no successful attempt to extract penicillin or to establish its therapeutic usefulness.

Fleming's paper reporting these findings was all but forgotten for ten years, and, as Brunel points out, "penicillin was never used for therapeutic purposes until the Oxford group, under Howard Florey, took up the problem; and Ernst Chain, the chemist of the team, devised a method of extraction and obtained, in 1940, in a stable form, pure penicillin . . ."

The first use of penicillin for treatment of a human patient, in England in 1941, was unsuccessful. The patient died because the available supply of penicillin was exhausted before he could make a complete recovery. Penicillin was recovered from the urine of early patients for re-use because of the scarcity of fresh drug.

By the middle of 1943, it was already clear that penicillin was not a very complex molecule; Florey and Abraham reported, "and during 1944 and 1945 many groups in the United States and England were trying to synthesize it." No satisfactory synthesis was then achieved, but "the Merck group and the Oxford workers, by condensing penicillamine with various oxazolones, obtained products which showed an activity of about 1 unit per mg. . . . The nature of the active product was finally proved by the Cornell group in 1946 . . ."

As Urdang has frequently pointed out, "Manufacturing pharmacy in America has been the child of wars." It was the unparalleled demands of World War II that stimulated research scientists and production engineers of the world, especially in Great Britain and the United States, to unprecedented advances that developed penicillin production from test-tube quantities to multiple tonnage.

Entry of the United States into the war late in 1941 brought urgent pressure for rapid development of production methods. There was a continuous exchange of information between British and American laboratories. Government agencies, academic institutions, and the pharmaceutical industry of both countries joined in the search for better strains of *Penicillium*, and better production methods.

The first penicillin made available for use, according to Colin and Silcox, was produced by surface fermentation in glass bottles. These bottles were capable of yielding approximately half a liter of broth after several days of fermentation. Even in small-scale operation, the number of bottles to be handled made the process unwieldy. It was necessary at that time to carry out this fermentation under conditions of shallow liquid depths, since the fermentation was aerobic.

Before long, however, microbiologists developed a mold strain capable of submerged production of pencillin which was adaptable to tank fermentation, provided an even flow of sterile air was introduced into the fermenting batch. Since that time, deep tank fermentors, equipped with air dispersers, agitators, heat and pressure control, have been used.

Further improvement of *Penicillium* strains, and of fermentation, filtration, extraction methods, and purification, vastly increased the yield of penicillin and the quality of the finished product.

From a rare, high-production-cost experimental drug, penicillin in the course of sixteen years became a mass-produced, low-profit pharmaceutical staple. Due to the inventiveness and ingenuity of the pharmaceutical industry, the price of bulk penicillin dropped from approximately $20 for 100,000 units to less than 5 cents per 100,000 units—a striking example of how the pharmaceutical profession serves its consuming public by producing more potent and effective medicines while bringing down the cost.

The impetus given to the search for new antibiotics during and since World War II has resulted in the report of literally hundreds of antimicrobial substances. Tested carefully in the research laboratories, by far the majority of these are discarded; but from time to time, new antibiotics and new varieties of older ones appear, to take their place among the weapons available to physicians in the constant fight against disease.

A strain of *Streptomyces griseus* capable of producing a new antibiotic, streptomycin, was first isolated in 1943, in the laboratories of Rutgers University under the direction of Dr. Selman A. Waksman. Its clinical importance was soon well established, and its usefulness, particularly against the tuberculosis organism, generally recognized. It, too, has undergone intensive research, and a number of variants have been developed by several manufacturers, though none has surpassed the parent compound.

One of the most dramatic chapters in antibiotic history concerns chloramphenicol, the first of the broad-spectrum antibiotics, pharmaceutical formulations of which are marketed by Parke, Davis & Company under the trademark Chloromycetin.® Chloramphenicol, which was reported in 1947, was obtained from culture fluids of a species of actinomycete isolated from a sample of soil collected from a mulched field near Caracas, Venezuela—one of the more than 6,000 soil samples examined in a screening program by Dr. Paul R. Burkholder of Yale University. This actinomycete was one of many such organisms passed on to the laboratories of Parke, Davis & Company for further evaluation under the cooperative program.

A team of research scientists, including mycologists, biochemists, organic chemists, physicists, and many others, grew this organism under various experimental conditions, and eventually isolated the pure, biologically active substance. Then the research teams divided. One group studied methods of growing the mold on a large scale submerged in aerated nutrient media in fermentation tanks. Another set out to translate the laboratory methods of isolation of crystalline chloramphenicol into pilot-plant terms preliminary to determining mass-production methods. A third team intensified studies of the effect of the new antibiotic against a wide range of bacteria, viruses, rickettsiae, fungi, and protozoa.

Still another team tested effects of the drug on animals. Chemists sought to determine the chemical structure of the unknown compound.

The chemists were successful in determining the chemical structure of chloramphenicol and subsequently in devising practical methods for creating the unique molecule from simple chemicals by synthetic means. Thus the identical chloramphenicol molecule could be made either by fermentation and extraction procedures or wholly by chemical synthesis. It was the first antibiotic to have been successfully produced on an industrial scale by chemical methods.

Meantime, the new antibiotic showed some remarkable properties. It was the first to reveal an effectiveness against a wide range of microorganisms—a truly broad-spectrum antibiotic. It overlapped parts of the spectra of penicillin and streptomycin, and also proved valuable against a number of other bacteria and rickettsiae, untouched by previously available medicine.

Equally dramatic was the clinical evaluation of choramphenicol. Among the microorganisms against which the drug showed particular activity was that of typhus fever. It is interesting that this untried antibiotic, produced by using an organism native to the soil of South America, should be particularly indicated for a disease which had periodically scourged that area of the world since history began.

It fell to the lot of Dr. Eugene H. Payne of the Parke-Davis Department of Clinical Investigation to try out the new drug on living patients. Epidemic typhus was raging in Bolivia, and Dr. Payne headed for La Paz with the world's total supply of chloramphenicol—less than half a pound. He administered Chloromycetin capsules to twenty-two typhus patients, all of whom recovered—including one man whose death certificate already had been signed, and awaited only notation as to time. The certificate was not used.

Shortly before, Dr. Joseph E. Smadel, of Walter Reed Hospital, had received a small sample of chloramphenicol from Parke-Davis, and had confirmed in his laboratory the antirickettsial activity previously observed at Parke-Davis. Later, during the winter of 1947-1948, a team of U. S. Army medical men, led by Drs. Smadel and Theodore E. Woodward, tested the drug against scrub typhus at Kuala Lumpur, Malaya. Again it proved a lifesaver for typhus victims—and also, uniquely, for those suffering from typhoid fever. Before long, many other diseases fell to chloramphenicol, and the new drug took its place among the highly useful members of the spectacularly successful antibiotic family of therapeutic agents.

A number of other broad-spectrum antibiotics soon followed, many of them originating from molds in the *actinomycete* group, among them aureomycin, terramycin, and the tetracycline off-shoots therefrom. It is impossible to estimate the number of lives that have been saved by this highly potent group of drugs evolved from lowly species of molds.

The world has an almost inexhaustible reservoir from which antibiotic substances may be sought. At least 50,000 kinds of molds are known; and the antibiotic potentialities of other natural groups have hardly been studied. Research teams have turned their attention less toward the discovery of numbers of new antibiotics, and more toward their qualitative selectivity for specific groups of disease-causing organisms as yet not controlled. As Dr. Martí-Ibáñez has stated, "Among those who have contributed most to the scientific crusade to master antibiotics are the research men in the pharmaceutical companies . . . Work in antibiotics is more international than in any other area of science, because its principal source lies in the earth . . ." Furthermore, the antibiotic age marked the introduction of a new era in pharmaceutical research. Individual investigations and chance discovery largely have been replaced by systematic investigations on which "chance" and "luck" are created and compelled by well-organized teams of scientists "who tear from the earth bactericidal powers which, like Sleeping Beauties, had lain dormant for thousands of years."

No single individual, laboratory, branch of science, or corporation can claim primary credit for the historical development that made antibiotics readily available and accepted therapeutic agents. There must be interdependence between research, production,

214

and professional application. Starting with fundamental research —including the efforts of the mycologist, the bacteriologist, and the chemist—the search for an antibiotic product progresses from fundamental soil or substrate sample from some corner of the world to petri dish culture; to test tube; to flask; to stair-step progression of sizes of fermentors, in which temperature, pressure, air, and agitation are closely controlled; to purification; to chemical and biological study; to animal and clinical evaluation. Then, if it be the one out of countless thousands of new compounds evaluated that shows promise of saving an infected host from microbial invaders without killing by its own toxicity, the end product of this long, exhaustive, and frequently discouraging chain of research links may be cautiously introduced through pharmaceutical channels for judicious prescription by physicians of the world. The spirit of Sir Alexander Fleming, whose keen observation launched not only a whole new field of disease-fighting drugs but also a new concept of the art of healing, indeed pervades every step in these new and pioneering procedures.

The impact of antibiotics upon research and manufacturing Pharmacy has been no more revolutionary than the impact upon retail Pharmacy. It has been said many times that about seventy-five per cent of the prescriptions written in the latter half of the 1950's could not have been filled in the early 1940's—because so many of the potent medicines were unknown in the previous decade.

As the availability of antibiotic preparations changed the prescription-writing habits of physicians, it changed the stocks and the professional practices in the prescription departments, and the economics of retail pharmacies. Volume of prescription practice, both in numbers and in dollar value, increased markedly. As Urdang has remarked, "the tendency toward changing the 'drug store' into a 'retail pharmacy' has received enormous uplift through the antibiotics."

With these changes, the professional responsibilities of retail pharmacists have increased. At the same time, remarkably, the cost of this greatly improved medical and pharmaceutical care is taking a smaller percentage of the wage-earner's dollar than in the

1930's; yet the benefits he and his family receive in return have continued to increase in the form of greater chance of longevity, of reduction of days lost from gainful employment, and of fewer days of confinement to bed or in convalescence.

One must agree with Dr. Waksman that it is still too early to write a closing chapter to antibiotics. They are too recent in origin and their development has been too spectacular to allow objective historical evaluation of them. Hundreds of laboratories throughout the world are engaged in the search for new antibiotics. New ones are discovered almost daily. Many problems still await solution.

A new chapter in the history of science is being written before our eyes.

WORLD EVENTS AND PHARMACY HISTORY

Dates, persons, and events of significance to the evolution of Pharmacy include:

1951	Nobel prize awarded to Max Theiler for his work on yellow fever.
1951	Effect of fluoride on development of dental caries discovered.
1952	Reserpine, blood pressure lowering drug, discovered.
1952	First open-heart operation by Baily.
1952	First hydrogen bomb explosion (Bikini).
1952	Restoration of Western European manufacturing facilities nearly complete (Marshall Plan).
1952	Peaceful uses of atomic energy encouraged by U.S.
1952	Nobel prize awarded to S. Waksman for his discovery of streptomycin.
1953	Nobel prize awarded to Krebs and Lipmann for their studies in carbohydrate metabolism and on coenzyme A.
1954	Launching of the first atomic-powered submarine *Nautilus*.
1954	Enders, Robbins and Weller shared Nobel prize for their work on tissue culture of poliomyelitis virus.
1955	Sir Alexander Fleming died.
1955	Poliomyelitis vaccine (Jonas Salk, U.S.) introduced.
1955	Nobel prizes awarded du Vigneaud and Theorell for their studies on the chemical synthesis of oxytocin, and on the oxygen transport system in living tissues.
1955	Canadian Academy of the History of Pharmacy founded.
1956	Research on the peaceful uses of nuclear fissionable material. Development of nuclear power stations.
1956	Weizäcker established the foundation for psychosomatic therapy.
1956	Nobel prize awarded to Forssmann, Cournand and Richards for their work on cardiac catheterization.
1957	First space satellite (Sputnik I).
1957	Nobel prizes awarded to Todd and Bovet for their studies on nucleotide coenzyme and on antihistamines and muscle relaxants.
1958	Nobel prizes awarded to Sanger for his work on synthesizing insulin and to Beadle, Tatum and Lederberg for their genetic research.
1959	Ochoa and Kornberg shared the Nobel prize for their work on synthesizing nucleic acids by means of enzymes.
1959	Polonski described the function of desoxyribonucleic acid on cellular mechanisms.
1959	Further research on seasonal and climatic factors in disease.
1959	Beginning of space medicine, physiologic problems, radiation protection.
1960	Introduction of the "laser."
1960	Nobel prize awarded to Burnet and Medawar for their studies on acquired immunity.
1961	First manned satellite (Gagarin).
1961	Nobel prize awarded to von Békésy for his research on sound wave stimulation of the cochlea.
1962	Nobel prize awarded to Francis Crick for his work in molecular biology.
1963	Research on nucleic acids in connection with viruses and cancer cells.
1963	Further improvements in electro-diagnostics (chronaximetry, encephalography, electrocardiography and cardioscopy).
1963	New developments in experimental pharmacology, drug, and irradiation therapy.
1963	New and improved surgical instruments: high performance endoscope; machine for suturing of blood vessels and intestines; high-frequency sound implements for coagulating and checking hemorrhage; laser rays used in skin grafting, cataract operations, tumor and cancer operations.
1963	Improvements in obstetrics: development of vacuum extractor and administration of oxytocics and analgetic agents reduces incidence of operative trauma.
1963	Improvements in psychiatry: great advances through fever and shock therapy; psychopharmacals replace leukotomy.
1963	Nobel prize awarded to Hodgkins, Huxley and Eccles for their work in neurologic research.

PHARMACY TODAY
AND TOMORROW

PHARMACY may be said to represent the sum total of all activities devoted to the preparation and distribution of drugs. As the twin profession of Medicine, it is, like Medicine, not a pure science based on particular laws of its own development and creation, but rather the beneficiary of whatever any of the sciences may offer for application to its purposes.

That sum total—the result of practical application of the thinking of the best minds in all sciences to the problem of discovering, creating, testing, evaluating, producing, and distributing disease-fighting and life-saving drug products—is the specialized contribution of the profession of Pharmacy to the public. Throughout all phases of this service, Pharmacy cooperates and closely collaborates with its sister profession, Medicine, in whose charge rests the responsibility for judicious use and prescription of the drugs, both new and old, that Pharmacy has evolved during the course of five millennia.

Along the course of these fifty centuries of service to mankind, Pharmacy, like Medicine, has come through many revolutions; weathered many storms; made mistakes; withstood setbacks; chafed under oppression; and enjoyed peaks of public respect. At times it has been shackled by ignorance and intolerance; at other times, liberated by science. It has brought many new things to the public by way of the prescriptions of physicians; yet Pharmacy has been quick to discard its offerings of yesteryear when they have been superseded by newer and better remedies. Pharmacy has been flexible and versatile, ever ready to learn new ways; to adapt

PHARMACY TODAY AND TOMORROW

Pharmacy, with its heritage of 50 centuries of service to mankind, has come to be recognized as one of the great professions. Like its twin, Medicine, it has come through many revolutions, has learned many things, has had to discard many of its older ways. Pharmacists are among the community's finest educated people. When today's retail pharmacist fills a prescription written by a physician, he provides a professional service incorporating the benefits of the work of pharmacists in all branches of the profession—education, research, development, standards, production, and distribution. Pharmacy's professional stature will continue to grow in the future as this great heritage and tradition of service is passed on from preceptor to apprentice, from teacher to student, from father to son.

219

itself to perform under and fulfill the ever-changing, ever-increasing responsibilities thrust upon it by the new conditions brought about by its own creations. From crude and simple herbs to galenicals; from raw minerals to chemicals; from whole plant drugs to extracts and components; from natural products to synthetic; from the haphazard to standards; from galenicals to chemotherapeutic agents to biologicals to hormones to antibiotics—through all these slow but inexorable changes, Pharmacy and the pharmacists who practice it have kept pace, and kept faith with the public to whose benefit all these fruits of scientific progress have accrued.

Throughout these centuries, Pharmacy has numbered among its practitioners well-informed men, well educated in the light of learning of their day, and men immersed not alone in the problems of their profession but capable as well of performing public, civic, and even political services. They have led reforms of their own profession and have been willing to expose themselves to the jeopardy of the law so that the people whom they served might be protected from the unscrupulous. They have imposed upon themselves codes of ethics and have disciplined themselves and their fellows so that their public trust might not suffer from venality. They have fostered laws that shut off the sales of popular products when public welfare was at stake. They have ever sought new ways of producing drugs, and of distributing them, that would relieve scarcities and make them more readily available to the public through proper channels at reduced cost. They have brought the products of world-wide research to the heart of every community and made them available on a few moments' notice, on presentation of a physician's prescription, to every man, woman and child in the greater part of the free world of today.

During the course of the years and these many evolutions of progress, Pharmacy, without losing its basic professional identity, has segmented itself into many specialized areas of service. Its major divisions include manufacturing, wholesaling, retailing, education, and law-enforcement. These, in turn, are divided into further subspecialties.

Manufacturing Pharmacy embraces an entire galaxy of specialized services related to Pharmacy. This includes research—with chemists, biochemists, physicists, physiologists, biologists, mycologists, toxicologists, and men and women possessed of knowledge and experience in many fields of activity from atomic to zoologic. Product development engages another corps of specialists; and production demands top talents and ingenuity of many persons, not the least of whom is the pharmaceutical engineer. Clinical evaluation of new drugs demands top performance from teams comprised both of physicians and pharmacists; and control measures test the mettle of many pharmacists every day. Then, to begin the chain of distribution, many more pharmacists serve as professional representatives to bring information about drug products to physicians and pharmacists. Over all, a corps of pharmaceutical administrators guides the destiny of huge organizations and formulates policies that focus all these specialized activities upon the major goal—service to the public.

Wholesalers in turn serve to bring together at a central point the products of thousands of manufacturers in many fields, for convenient redistribution to hundreds of retail pharmacies, performing many services that contribute eventually to the benefit and convenience of the public at large.

As the chain of distribution reaches out to the communities where people live, ultimate distribution to the consumer proceeds through retail pharmacies and hospital pharmacies. Here the community public most often sees the face of Pharmacy; and here is where the public's opinion of Pharmacy is moulded. Whether hospital pharmacy, professional pharmacy, or general service retail pharmacy, the spirit of Pharmacy and the desire to practice its "art and mystery" will be found in the hearts of the professional men and women who guide its operations and serve its patrons.

Pharmaceutical education has kept pace with all of its contemporary sciences and professions. As professional responsibilities increased, traditional apprenticeship yielded in large part to academic training; and formal courses in education in Pharmacy have been broadened, expanded, specialized, and lengthened to keep pace with the developments of science and the needs of the public. Today, graduation from a recognized college of Pharmacy is a requisite to admission to the practice of Pharmacy in virtually all modern nations of the world. To train the graduate to meet the responsibilities placed upon him by his community, state, province, or nation, his teachers must be specialists in phases of all modern sciences.

Law enforcement has opened a broad field of service to pharmacists, not only in advising and policing the various facets of Pharmacy, but in applying the broad, coordinated knowledge learned in Pharmacy to problems in other fields of public service and protection. In the field of legislation and administration, pharmacists frequently have served well and with distinction.

Whenever a man or woman carries a prescription from the office of a physician into a retail pharmacy, or a nurse delivers a written prescription to a hospital pharmacy, the simple, everyday act brings to focus upon the personal problem signified by the prescription all of the forces of Pharmacy previously described. However simple or complex may be the cryptic formula written upon the slip under the age-old ℞ sign—there goes into it the essence of pharmaceutical service, distilled from the experience of countless generations of pharmacists. This becomes the hidden ingredient—indeed, the "mystery" that goes along with the "art" of today's modern pharmacist.

The art of the pharmacist is not a lost art today, despite cynical statements that may be heard from time to time. The pharmacist's art today is in his knowledge, rather than in the skill of his hands. His responsibilities today are far greater than those which were placed upon his father or grandfather, proud though they were of the elegance of their galenicals and the perfection of their hand-made pills.

What of the pharmacist of today? What is his status? What is his plight? What future lies before him?

Despite the dissatisfaction to be heard upon occasion; despite the griping and self-commiseration that may be heard when pharmacists get together for a good, healthy purge of mental stasis; despite the very real troubles and problems that confront Pharmacy as a profession and its practitioners as individuals, certain facts stand out.

Pharmacy, despite its troubles, today has advanced far beyond any position it has ever previously occupied in world civilization. Its practitioners enjoy as high a level of public respect as they have ever been accorded; their economic position, in whatever field of Pharmacy they may practice, has never been surpassed; and their future prospects never were brighter. Despite the impact of constant change—the stimulant that probably has done most to prevent Pharmacy from becoming static—Pharmacy has an unlimited horizon before it.

The opportunities for public service that lie ahead for today's pharmacists, and the younger generations to follow, are tremendous. Furthermore, pharmacists of no preceding age had such excellent facilities, such fine tools, such opportunities for education, and such coordinated cooperation among the specialists within Pharmacy, as have the young men and women entering the profession today, tomorrow, or next year.

What does this heritage of Pharmacy, this evolution of a great profession, mean to the public? What does it mean to the man on the street, the woman in the home, the child at play or in school?

It means that the public—the people who live in our communities and patronize retail pharmacies—have gained a tremendous stake. They have inherited an unprecedented improvement in their opportunity for better health, happiness, and increased longevity. Largely through the contributions of the pharmaceutical profession in cooperation with the medical profession, people today have nearly twice the life expectancy that they would have had at the beginning of the twentieth century.

Neither kings nor potentates nor presidents nor dictators nor millionaires, in 1900, or 1920, or even 1940, could possibly have bought, demanded, commanded, stolen, usurped, or appropriated for their own use the remedies that were available to every man, woman and child in the mid-'50's through any retail pharmacy almost anywhere in the free world. These potent pharmaceutical products simply were not known or made, even as World War II exploded upon the scene. Yet today, any man, with the cooperation of his physician and pharmacist, easily may secure the benefits of the scientific advances of recent decades for himself and his family.

Pharmacy's stature as a profession, and the status, both professional and economic, of individual pharmacists, will continue to grow as long as they continue to embrace change as the tonic that pours new vigor into its blood stream; and as long as satisfactory service of the public's desires and best interests continues to be its guiding star. There is neither time nor place in Pharmacy's future for sighing over the good old days. A backward look at history and a consciousness of our heritage must serve only to let us know where we are, and to point the way, with safeguards of experience, to new horizons.

Pharmacy, today and tomorrow, will continue to be a great profession; and to grow, as this great heritage and tradition of service is passed on from preceptor to apprentice, from teacher to student, and from father to son.

ACKNOWLEDGMENTS

ACKNOWLEDGMENT of most helpful assistance, and sincere thanks, are extended to the many persons, experts in their fields, who have assisted in the development and authentication of these stories, and of the pictures which accompany them. Particular thanks are due Drs. Glenn Sonnedecker, Director, and George Urdang, Director Emeritus, American Institute of the History of Pharmacy, Madison, Wisconsin, whose advice, assistance, and criticism, have guided the author-artist team throughout the project, and without which the task would have been almost insurmountable.

This project also was dependent in large measure upon the interest, support, and cooperation extended it by Parke-Davis personnel. Among those who contributed advice, encouragement, and assistance were: President Harry J. Loynd; Vice Presidents Carl Johnson, Graydon L. Walker, W. R. Jeeves, T. C. Anderson, and C. D. Smith; Dr. J. P. Gray; Walter L. Griffith, John A. MacCartney, J. R. Anderson, Gertrude Losie, L. Crane, Stella Dill, Clara Banfield and D. Gilmore.

Other persons who gave freely of their time, knowledge, advice, and assistance in connection with various subjects, include the following:

Before the Dawn of History
Richard A. Martin, Curator of Near Eastern Archaeology, The Chicago Natural History Museum, Chicago, Illinois.

Pharmacy In Ancient Babylonia
F. W. Geers, Ph.D., Associate Professor of Assyriology, The Oriental Institute, University of Chicago, Chicago, Illinois.

Alexander Heidel, Ph.D., Research Associate, The Oriental Institute, University of Chicago, Chicago, Illinois.

Pharmacy In Ancient China
Dr. Arthur Hummel, Chief, and Joseph Wang and Hsu Liang, Orientalia Division, Library of Congress, Washington, D. C.

The Oriental Institute, University of Chicago, Chicago, Illinois.

Dr. Ilza Veith, Associate Professor of the History of Medicine, Department of Medicine, University of Chicago, Chicago, Illinois.

Days of the Papyrus Ebers
Richard A. Martin, Curator of Near Eastern Archaeology, The Chicago Natural History Museum, Chicago, Illinois.

K. C. Seele, Ph.D., Egyptologist, The Oriental Institute, University of Chicago, Chicago, Illinois.

Ralph Setton, Ph.D., National Center for Scientific Research, Paris, France.

Theophrastus—Father of Botany
Detroit Public Library, Detroit, Michigan.

Dr. Mary Swindler, Visiting Professor of Fine Arts, University of Michigan, Ann Arbor, Michigan.

Dr. Dietrich von Bothmer, Associate Curator, Greek-Roman Section, Metropolitan Museum of Art, New York, New York.

The Royal Toxicologist—Mithridates VI
Detroit Public Library, Detroit, Michigan.

The Metropolitan Museum of Art, New York, New York.

Dr. Mary Swindler, Visiting Professor of Fine Arts, University of Michigan, Ann Arbor, Michigan.

Terra Sigillata

Detroit Public Library, Detroit, Michigan.

Dr. George Lechler, Anthropologist and Assistant Professor of History, Wayne State University, Detroit, Michigan.

Dr. Dietrich von Bothmer, Associate Curator, Greek-Roman Section, Metropolitan Museum of Art, New York, New York.

Dioscorides—A Scientist Looks at Drugs

Detroit Public Library, Detroit, Michigan.

Dr. George Lechler, Anthropologist and Assistant Professor of History, Wayne State University, Detroit, Michigan.

Dr. Dietrich von Bothmer, Associate Curator, Greek-Roman Section, Metropolitan Museum of Art, New York, New York.

Galen—Experimenter In Drug Compounding

Detroit Public Library, Detroit, Michigan.

Dr. George Lechler, Anthropologist and Assistant Professor of History, Wayne State University, Detroit, Michigan.

Metropolitan Museum of Art, New York, New York.

Damian and Cosmas

Francis W. Robinson, Curator of Ancient and Medieval Art, The Detroit Institute of Arts, Detroit, Michigan.

Mrs. A. C. Weibel, Curator-emeritus of Textiles and Islamic Art, The Detroit Institute of Arts, Detroit, Michigan.

Monastic Pharmacy

The Cloisters, New York, New York.

Canon Asztrik Gabriel, O. Praem, Professor, The Mediaeval Institute, University of Notre Dame, South Bend, Indiana.

Rose Green, Director, Index of Christian Art, Princeton University, Princeton, New Jersey.

Esther Ann Huebner, Gardener, The Cloisters, Metropolitan Museum of Art, New York City.

Metropolitan Museum of Art, New York, New York.

The First Apothecary Shop

Francis W. Robinson, Curator of Ancient and Medieval Art, The Detroit Institute of Arts, Detroit, Michigan.

Dr. Gustave E. von Grunebaum, Orientalist and Professor of Araby, Oriental Institute, University of Chicago, Chicago, Illinois.

Mrs. A. C. Weibel, Curator-emeritus of Textiles and Islamic Art, The Detroit Institute of Arts, Detroit, Michigan.

Avicenna—The "Persian Galen"

Hodge Magarian, Oriental Rug Expert, Detroit, Michigan.

Francis W. Robinson, Curator of Ancient and Medieval Art, The Detroit Institute of Arts, Detroit, Michigan.

G. A. Vahid, Counselor of the Iranian Embassy, Washington, D.C.

Dr. Gustave E. von Grunebaum, Orientalist and Professor of Araby, Oriental Institute, University of Chicago, Chicago, Illinois.

Mrs. A. C. Weibel, Curator-emeritus of Textiles and Islamic Art, The Detroit Institute of Arts, Detroit, Michigan.

Separation of Pharmacy and Medicine

Francis W. Robinson, Curator of Ancient and Medieval Art, The Detroit Institute of Arts, Detroit, Michigan.

The First Official Pharmacopoeia

Francis W. Robinson, Curator of Ancient and Medieval Art, The Detroit Institute of Arts, Detroit, Michigan.

The Society of Apothecaries

Dr. Giles E. Dawson, Curator of Books and Manuscripts, Folger Shakespearean Library, Washington, D.C.

Paul L. Grigaut, Associate Curator of Western Art, The Detroit Institute of Arts, Detroit, Michigan.

Dr. Louis B. Wright, Director, Folger Shakespearean Library, Washington, D.C.

Louis Hébert

Louis Carrier, Leetham, Simpson, Ltd., Montreal, Canada. (A descendant of L. Hébert.)

Gerard Morriset, Associate Curator of the Museum of the Province of Quebec, Quebec, Canada.

Staff member of The Habitation, Annapolis Royal, Nova Scotia, Canada.

The Governor Who Healed the Sick

Dr. Willis T. Bradley, Massachusetts College of Pharmacy, Boston, Massachusetts.

The Essex Institute, Salem, Massachusetts.

Charles Childs, Childs Gallery, Boston, Massachusetts.

Stephen T. Riley, Librarian, The Massachusetts Historical Society, Boston, Massachusetts.

The Marshall Apothecary

Edward Alexander, Robert Hoke, and Norman Marshall, Colonial Williamsburg, Virginia.

Dr. Ivor Griffith, Dean, Philadelphia College of Pharmacy and Science, Philadelphia, Pennsylvania.

Historical Society of Pennsylvania, Philadelphia, Pennsylvania.

Dr. E. M. Riley, U. S. National Park Service, Philadelphia, Pennsylvania.

The First Hospital Pharmacy

Mrs. J. W. Hamner, Hugh Mercer Apothecary Shop, Fredericksburg, Virginia.

Historical Society of Pennsylvania, Philadelphia, Pennsylvania.

The Pennsylvania Hospital, Philadelphia, Pennsylvania.

Dr. E. M. Riley, U. S. National Park Service, Philadelphia, Pennsylvania.

Carl Wilhelm Scheele

Bengt Bengtsson, Nordiska Musee, Stockholm, Sweden.

Donmarks Apotekerforen, Copenhagen, Denmark.

Lauritz Gentz, Apothecary, Stockholm, Sweden.

Gunnar Krook, Librarian of the Apothekar-societenen, Stockholm, Sweden.

Ivan Östholm, Apothecary, Apotekens Kompositionslaboratorium, Stockholm, Sweden.

America's First Apothecary General

Stephen T. Riley, Librarian, The Massachusetts Historical Society, Boston, Massachusetts.

Agnes Scanlan, Veterans Association, First Corps Cadets, Boston, Massachusetts.

John G. Weld, Head Custodian, The Bostonian Society, Boston, Massachusetts.

Warren G. Wheeler, Assistant Librarian, The Massachusetts Historical Society, Boston, Massachusetts.

First of the Alkaloid Chemists

Dr. Gunther Kerstein, Hameln, Germany.

Eva von Schilling, Hameln, Germany.

Caventou, Pelletier, and Quinine

Professor C. Bedel, Faculté de Pharmacie, Université de Paris, Paris, France.

Dr. Maurice Bouvet, President, Union Mondiale des Sociétés d'Histoire Pharmaceutique, Paris, France.

Lieutenant de Tretaigne, Archiviste, Hôtel des Invalides, Paris, France.

Dr. D. A. Wittop Koning, Pharmacist, Amsterdam, Holland.

American Pharmacy Builds
Its Foundations

Charles Dawant, Brussels, Belgium.

Dr. Ivor Griffith, Dean of Philadelphia College of Pharmacy and Science, and members of his staff, Philadelphia, Pennsylvania.

Mr. and Mrs. Charles E. Jackson, Custodians of Carpenters' Hall, Philadelphia, Pennsylvania.

The Shakers & Medicinal Herbs

Dr. Charles C. Adams, Director-Emeritus, New York State Museum, Albany, New York.

Dr. Edward D. Andrews, New York State Museum, Albany, New York.

Brother Ricardo Belden, Hancock Community, Pittsfield, Massachusetts.

Sister Grace Dahm, Hancock Community, Pittsfield, Massachusetts.

Sister Mary Dahm, Hancock Community, Pittsfield, Massachusetts.

William L. Lassiter, Senior Curator of History and Art, New York State Museum, Albany, New York.

Sister Jennie M. Wells, Hancock Community, Pittsfield, Massachusetts.

The American Pharmaceutical
Association

Dr. Alex Berman, American Institute of the History of Pharmacy, Madison, Wisconsin.

Robert P. Fischelis, former Secretary, The American Pharmaceutical Association, Washington, D.C.

George Griffenhagen, Curator, Division of Medicine and Public Health, Smithsonian Institution, Washington, D.C.

European & American Pharmacy Meet

Professor C. Bedel, Faculté de Pharmacie, Université de Paris, Paris, France.

Dr. Maurice Bouvet, President, Union Mondiale des Sociétés d'Histoire Pharmaceutique, Paris, France.

Mrs. Elizabeth Johnson, Librarian, Philadelphia College of Pharmacy and Science, Philadelphia, Pennsylvania.

The Father of American Pharmacy

Dr. E. Fullerton Cook, Media, Pennsylvania.

Robert P. Fischelis, former Secretary, the American Pharmaceutical Association, Washington, D.C.

Dr. Ivor Griffith, Dean, Philadelphia College of Pharmacy and Science, Philadelphia, Pennsylvania.

Historical Society of Pennsylvania, Philadelphia, Pennsylvania.

Mrs. Elizabeth Johnson, Librarian, Philadelphia College of Pharmacy and Science, Philadelphia, Pennsylvania.

A Revolution in Pharmaceutical
Education

F. Clever Bald, Assistant Director, Michigan Historical Collections, Ann Arbor, Michigan.

Dean-Emeritus Edward W. Kraus, College of Pharmacy, University of Michigan, Ann Arbor, Michigan.

Dean Tom C. Rowe, College of Pharmacy of the University of Michigan, Ann Arbor, Michigan.

The Pharmacopoeia Comes of Age

Dr. E. Fullerton Cook, Media, Pennsylvania.

Dr. Lloyd C. Miller, Director of Pharmacopoeial Revision, New York, New York.

Dr. Adley B. Nichols, Secretary, The United States Pharmacopoeial Convention, Inc., New York, New York.

The Standardization of Pharmaceuticals

William P. Cusick, Director of Quality Control, Parke, Davis & Company, Detroit, Michigan.

Fabian A. Maurina, Director of Analytical Laboratories, Parke, Davis & Company, Detroit, Michigan.

Dr. Hervey C. Parke, Products Development Department, Parke, Davis & Company, Detroit, Michigan.

Dr. Frank O. Taylor, South Fort Mitchell, Kentucky.

Wresting the Jungle's Secrets

Mrs. W. A. Couper, Long Boat Key, Florida.

Dr. E. E. Leuallen, Dean, College of Pharmacy, Columbia University, New York.

Mrs. K. D. Muir, Grand Rapids, Michigan.

Chester H. Newkirk, Registrar, The Newark Museum, Newark, New Jersey.

Dr. Frank O. Taylor, South Fort Mitchell, Kentucky.

Mrs. M. C. von Hoegen, Oneco, Florida.

Mrs. Lucita Wait, Fairchild Tropical Garden, Coconut Grove, Florida.

Stanislas Limousin—Pharmacal Inventor

Professor C. Bedel, Faculté de Pharmacie, Université de Paris, Paris, France.

Dr. Maurice Bouvet, President, Union Mondiale des Sociétés d'Histoire Pharmaceutique, Paris, France.

Monsieur P. des Gachons, Marne, France.

Lieutenant de Tretaigne, Archiviste, Hôtel des Invalides, Paris, France.

Dr. D. A. Wittop Koning, Pharmacist, Amsterdam, Holland.

Era of Biologicals

Dr. George Brigham, Parke, Davis & Company, Detroit, Michigan.

Dr. F. O. Taylor, South Fort Mitchell, Kentucky.

Dr. R. H. Wilson, Rochester, Michigan.

Development of Chemotherapy

M. Jacques Trefouël, Director, and Mme. Trefouël, l'Institut Pasteur, Paris, France.

Pharmaceutical Research

Dr. Ivor Griffith, Dean, Philadelphia College of Pharmacy and Science, Philadelphia, Pennsylvania.

Drs. Leon A. Sweet, George Rieveschl, Harry M. Crooks, J. M. Vandenbelt, C. A. Bratton, F. D. Stimpert, Horst Schneider, and John Controulis, Parke, Davis & Company, Detroit, Michigan.

Dr. Frank O. Taylor, South Fort Mitchell, Kentucky.

Pharmaceutical Manufacturing Comes of Age

Thomas C. Anderson, Vice President, Parke, Davis & Company, Detroit, Michigan.

Homer C. Fritsch, Executive Vice President, Parke, Davis & Company, Detroit, Michigan.

Dr. F. O. Taylor, South Fort Mitchell, Kentucky.

The Era of Antibiotics

George Griffenhagen, Curator, Division of Medicine and Public Health of the Smithsonian Institution, Washington, D.C.

Dr. Theodore G. Klumpp, President, Winthrop Laboratories.

Dr. John N. McDonnell, vice president, Schering Corp., Bloomfield, New Jersey.

Leslie O. Smith, Manager, Parke, Davis & Company, Ltd., Hounslow, Middlesex, England.

Dr. Leon A. Sweet, Thomas C. Anderson, and Dr. John Ehrlich, Parke, Davis & Company, Detroit, Michigan.

REFERENCES

MANY SOURCES of information, both published and unpublished, have contributed to the factual background for stories and paintings in this series. Due acknowledgment and thanks are extended to authors and sources. Persons interested in further information on the subjects covered, or in background information, may find these sources worthy of consultation. Except for general references, sources are listed under the subject headings used in this book.

General References

The following sources of general information concerning the History of Pharmacy have proved to be of great value:

Castiglioni, A., *A History of Medicine*. New York, Alfred A. Knopf, 1947.

Garrison, Fielding H., *An Introduction to the History of Medicine*, Ed. 4. Philadelphia, W. B. Saunders Co., 1929.

Kremers, Edward, and Urdang, George, *History of Pharmacy*, Ed. 2. Philadelphia, J. B. Lippincott Co., 1951.

LaWall, Charles H., *The Curious Lore of Drugs and Medicines*. Garden City, Garden City Publishing Company, 1927.

Sigerist, Henry E., *A History of Medicine*, Vol. 1. New York, Oxford University Press, 1955.

Before the Dawn of History

Leake, C.D., *Ancient Egyptian Therapy*. Ciba Symposia, 1:311-322, 1940.

Thompson, C.J.S., *The Mystery and Art of the Apothecary*. London, John Lane, The Bodley Head, Ltd., 1929.

Pharmacy In Ancient Babylonia

Chiera, Edward, *They Wrote On Clay*. Chicago, University of Chicago Press, 1938.

Thompson, C.J.S., *The Mystery and Art of the Apothecary*. London, John Lane, The Bodley Head, Ltd., 1929.

Pharmacy In Ancient China

Hume, E.H., *The Chinese Way in Medicine*. Baltimore, The Johns Hopkins Press, 1940.

Wong, K. Chimin, and Wu, Lien-Teh, *The History of Chinese Medicine*. Tientsin, China, The Tientsin Press, 1932.

Days of the Papyrus Ebers

Breasted, James H., *The Edwin Smith Surgical Papyrus*, 2 Vols. Chicago, The University of Chicago Press, 1930.

Grapow, H., *Untersuchungen über die altagyptischen Papyri, I. Teil, Mitteilungen*, Vorderasiatischaegyptische Gesells, 1935.

Jonckheere, Frans, *The "Preparer of Remedies" in the Organization of Egyptian Pharmacy*. Deutsche Akademie der Wissenschaften zu Berlin Institut für Orientforschung, Nr. 29. Berlin, Akademie-Verlag, 1955.

Leake, C.D., *Ancient Egyptian Therapy*. Ciba Symposia, 1:311-322, 1940.

Schelenz, H., *Geschichte der Pharmazie*. Berlin, J. Springer, 1904.

Winkler, Ludwig, *Das Apothekergewicht*. Pharm. Monatshefte, 5:6, 1924.

Theophrastus—Father of Botany

Cohen, M.R., and Drabkin, I.E., *A Source Book in Greek Science*. New York, McGraw-Hill Book Co., Inc., 1948.

The Royal Toxicologist—Mithridates VI

Thompson, C.J.S., *The Mystery and Art of the Apothecary*. London, John Lane, The Bodley Head, Ltd., 1929.

Wootton, A.C., *Chronicles of Pharmacy*. London, MacMillan & Co., Ltd., 1910.

Terra Sigillata

Thompson, C.J.S., *The Mystery and Art of the Apothecary*. London, John Lane, The Bodley Head, Ltd., 1929.

Wootton, A.C., *Chronicles of Pharmacy*. London, MacMillan & Co., Ltd., 1910.

Dioscorides—A Scientist Looks at Drugs

Gunther, Robert T., *The Greek Herbal of Dioscorides*. Oxford Press, Oxford University, 1934.

Tschirch, Alexander, *Handbuch der Pharmakognosie*, Ed. 2. Leipzig, B. Tauchnitz, 1930.

Galen—Experimenter In Drug Compounding

Diepgen, Paul, *Geschichte der Medizin*. Berlin, W. de Gruyter, 1949.

Green, Robert M., *A Translation of Galen's Hygiene*. Springfield, Ill., Charles C Thomas, 1951.

Meunier, L., *Essai sur Galien et le Galenisme*. In Janus; Archives Internationales pour l'Histoire de la Médecine et la Géographie Médicale, 9:270-284; 313-324, 1904.

Sarton, George, *Galen of Pergamon*. Lawrence, Kansas, University of Kansas Press, 1954.

Damian and Cosmas

Artelt, Walter, *Die Kosmas und Damian Forschung*, (summary). Jubiläumstagung der Internationalen Gesellschaft für Geschichte der Pharmazie. Pharmazeutische Zeitung, 87 (1951), 766 f.

Thompson, C.J.S., *The Mystery and Art of the Apothecary*. London, John Lane, The Bodley Head, Ltd., 1929.

Wootton, A.C., *Chronicles of Pharmacy*. London, MacMillan & Co., Ltd., 1910.

Monastic Pharmacy

Catholic Encyclopedia. New York, Catholic Encyclopedia Press, 1922.

Thompson, C.J.S., *The Mystery and Art of the Apothecary*. London, John Lane, The Bodley Head, Ltd., 1929.

The First Apothecary Shop

Hamarneh, Sami, *The Rise of Professional Pharmacy in Islam*. Medical History, Vol. 6, No. 1, Jan., 1962.

Thompson, C.J.S., *The Mystery and Art of the Apothecary*. London, John Lane, The Bodley Head, Ltd., 1929.

Tschirch, Alexander, *Handbuch der Pharmakognosie*, Ed. 2. Leipzig, B. Tauchnitz, 1930.

Avicenna—The "Persian Galen"

Hekmat, Ali-Asghar, *The Millennium of a Great Man*. An address. Iran, 1952.

Sarton, George, *Introduction to the History of Science*. Baltimore, published for the Carnegie Institution of Washington by Williams & Wilkins, 1927.

Separation of Pharmacy and Medicine

Thompson, C.J.S., *The Mystery and Art of the Apothecary*. London, John Lane, The Bodley Head, Ltd., 1929.

Wootton, A.C., *Chronicles of Pharmacy*. London, MacMillan & Co., Ltd., 1910.

Yerby, Frank, *The Saracen Blade*. New York, Dial Press, 1952.

The First Official Pharmacopoeia

Thompson, C.J.S., *The Mystery and Art of the Apothecary*. London, John Lane, The Bodley Head, Ltd., 1929.

Wootton, A.C., *Chronicles of Pharmacy*. London, MacMillan & Co., Ltd., 1910.

The Society of Apothecaries

Thompson, C.J.S., *The Mystery and Art of the Apothecary*. London, John Lane, The Bodley Head, Ltd., 1929.

Wootton, A.C., *Chronicles of Pharmacy*. London, MacMillan & Co., Ltd., 1910.

Louis Hébert

Birkett, H.J., *The History of Medicine in the Province of Quebec, 1535-1838*. New York, 1908.

Bishop, Morris, *Champlain, The Life of Fortitude*. New York, Knopf, 1948.

Carlton, M., *Louis Hébert*. Johns Hopkins Hospital Bulletin, 24:158, 1914.

Couillard Déspres, Azarie, *Louis Hébert, Premier Colon Canadian et sa Famille*. Lille, Paris, Société Saint-Augustin, Descleé, de Brouwer & Cie, 1913.

The Governor Who Healed the Sick

Bradley, Will T., *Medical Practices of the New England Aborigines*. Journal of the American Pharmaceutical Association, 25:146, 1936.

Viets, Henry Rouse, *A Brief History of Medicine in Massachusetts*. Boston, Houghton Mifflin, 1930.

Winthrop, John, *Winthrop Papers*, Vol. 3, 1631-1637. Boston, Massachusetts Historical Society, 1943.

The Marshall Apothecary

England, Joseph W., *The First Century of the Philadelphia College of Pharmacy, 1821-1921*. Philadelphia, 1922.

Journal of the Philadelphia College of Pharmacy, 1:255-6, 1830.

The First Hospital Pharmacy

Carson, Joseph, *History of the Medical Department of the University of Pennsylvania*. Philadelphia, 1869.

England, Joseph W., *The Debt of American Pharmacy to Benjamin Franklin and His protégé, John Morgan*. Journal of the American Pharmaceutical Association, 21:1171-1177, 1932.

Franklin, Benjamin, *Some account of the Pennsylvania Hospital from its rise to the beginning of the fifth month, called May, 1754*. Philadelphia. Privately printed by B. Franklin and D. Hall, 1754.

Pennsylvania Hospital Minute Book No. 1. Philadelphia, 1751.

Carl Wilhelm Scheele

Urdang, George, *The Apothecary-Chemist, Carl Wilhelm Scheele*. American Institute of the History of Pharmacy, Madison, Wisconsin, 1942.

America's First Apothecary General

Kebler, Lyman F., *Andrew Craigie, the First Apothecary General of the United States*. Journal of the American Pharmaceutical Association, 17:63-74, 167-178, 1928.

Kebler, Lyman F., *Craigie, Andrew*. Dictionary of American Biography, Vol. 4, 497-8. New York, Charles Scribner's Sons, 1937.

Lefferts, Charles Mackubin, *Uniforms of the American, British, French and German armies in the War of the American Revolution, 1775-1783*. New York, The New York Historical Society, 1926.

Pratt, Frederick Haven, *The Craigies*. Cambridge, The Cambridge Historical Society, 1942.

First of the Alkaloid Chemists

Kroemecke, Franz, *Fr. W. Sertürner*. Jena, 1925.

Thompson, C.J.S., *The Mystery and Art of the Apothecary*. London, John Lane, The Bodley Head, Ltd., 1929.

Caventou, Pelletier, and Quinine

Pelletier, P.J., *Lettre aux mêmes Rédacteurs.* Annales de Chimie et de Physique, 16 (1821), 222.

Pelletier, P.J., and Caventou, J.B., *Recherches Chimiques sur les Quinquinas*. Annales de Chimie et de Physique, 15 (1820), 289-318.

Seguin, Armand, *á MM. les Rédacteurs . . .* (a letter on cinchona analysis). Annales de Chimie et de Physique, 16 (1821), 221.

American Pharmacy Builds Its Foundations

England, Joseph W., *The First Century of the Philadelphia College of Pharmacy, 1821-1921*. Philadelphia, 1922.

Griffith, Ivor, *Philadelphia College of Pharmacy and Science*. Tile and Till, Sept.-Oct., 1951.

Levick, James J., *Daniel B. Smith, First Corresponding Secretary of the Historical Society of Pennsylvania*. Pennsylvania Magazine of History and Biography, 7:309-316, 1883.

Peterson, Charles E., *Carpenters' Hall*. Transactions of the American Philosophical Society, Vol. 43, Part 1. Philadelphia, 1953.

Philadelphia College of Pharmacy, *Minute Book*, 1821.

Smith, Daniel B., *Address of the President*. Journal of the Philadelphia College of Pharmacy, 1:241-261, 1830.

The Shakers and Medicinal Herbs

Andrews, Edward D., *The Community Industries of the Shakers*. Albany, New York, The University of the State of New York, 1933.

Andrews, Edward D., *The New York Shakers and their Industries*. Albany, Circular 2, The New York State Museum, 1930.

New Lebanon; its Physic Gardens, and their Products. American Journal of Pharmacy, 23:386-388, 1851; 24:88-91, 1852.

Piercy, Harry D., *Shaker Medicines*. Ohio State Archaeological and Historical Quarterly, 63: No. 4, 1954.

The Shakers. Harper's New Monthly Magazine, Vol. 15, No. 86, July, 1857.

The American Pharmaceutical Association

Centennial Meeting of the American Pharmaceutical Association, *Program*. Philadelphia, 1952.

England, Joseph W., *The First Century of the Philadelphia College of Pharmacy, 1821-1921*. Philadelphia, 1922.

The Founders of the American Pharmaceutical Association. Journal of the A.Ph.A., Vol. 13, No. 10, 1952.

Fuller, H.J., *The Changing Role of the Professions in Society*. Canadian Pharmaceutical Journal, May 1, 1954.

Muldoon, Hugh C., *The Strengths of Pharmacy*. Address, Remington Honor Medal Dinner, Dec. 7, 1953.

Proceedings of the National Pharmaceutical Convention, 1852, Facsimile copy. The American Pharmaceutical Association, Washington, D.C., 1952.

European and American Pharmacy Meet

Journal de Pharmacie et de Chimie, 5th series, Vol. 6, p. 291, 1867.

Procter, William, Jr., and Faber, John, *Report of the Delegates to the International Pharmaceutical Congress, at Paris*. Proceedings of the American Pharmaceutical Association, Vol. 15, 314-318, Washington, D. C., 1867.

Procter, William, Jr., *Report of the International Pharmaceutical Congress, Paris, 1867*. American Journal of Pharmacy, Vol. 15, p. 280.

Urdang, George, *International Pharmacy*. American Druggist, Vol. 108, No. 5, 1943.

Urdang, George, *Development of Modern Pharmacy in the United States*. Merck Report, Vol. 56, No. 4, Oct., 1947.

The Father of American Pharmacy

Memoir of William Procter, Jr. American Journal of Pharmacy, Nov., 1874.

Procter, William, Jr., *Editorial*. American Journal of Pharmacy, March 1, 1871, p. 134.

Procter, William, Jr., *The Retiring Editor to His Friends and Readers.* American Journal of Pharmacy, Vol. 43, April 1, 1871, p. 186.

A Revolution In Pharmaceutical Education

Briggs, W. Paul, *Changing Patterns in Pharmaceutical Education.* The Merck Report, July, 1952.

Campbell, Edward D., *History of the Chemical Laboratory of the University of Michigan, 1856-1916.* Ann Arbor, The University, 1916.

Deno, Richard A., *University of Michigan College of Pharmacy.* Tile and Till, Dec., 1953.

Parrish, Edward, *A Treatise on Pharmacy.* Philadelphia, Blanchard and Lea, 1864.

Prescott, A.B., *Silas H. Douglas as Professor of Chemistry and Pharmacy.* Pharmaceutical Review, 21:359, 1903.

Sonnedecker, Glenn, *Science in American Pharmaceutical Education in the 19th Century.* The American Journal of Pharmaceutical Education, Vol. XV, No. 2, pp. 185-217, April, 1951.

Stocking, Charles H., *Albert B. Prescott.* American Journal of Pharmaceutical Education, 12:388-9, 1948.

The Pharmacopoeia Comes of Age

The Journal of Edward Robinson Squibb, 2 Vols. Privately printed.

Proceedings of the American Pharmaceutical Association, Vol. 25, p. 531, 1877.

Remington, Joseph Price, *In Memoriam.* American Journal of Pharmacy, 91:65-121, Feb., 1918.

Remington, Joseph Price, *In Memory of Edward Robinson Squibb.* Reprint from Minutes of the Committee of Revision of the United States Pharmacopoeia, 1900-1910.

Rice, Charles, *In Memoriam.* Philadelphia, J. B. Lippincott Company, 1904.

Squibb, E.R., ed., *Ephemeris of Materia Medica, Pharmacy, Therapeutics and Collateral Information.* Brooklyn, N.Y., Vol. 1, 1882-1883.

Squibb, E.R., *In Memoriam.* Minutes of the Committee of Revision of the United States Pharmacopoeia, 1900-1910.

Squibb, E.R., *Report on the U.S.P.* Proceedings of the American Pharmaceutical Association, Vol. 25, 531, Washington, D.C., 1877.

The United States Pharmacopoeia, *Historical Introductions, and Abstracts of Proceedings,* (various editions).

Urdang, George, *The Development of Pharmacopoeias.* Bulletin of the World Health Organization, 4:577-603, 1951.

Urdang, George, *The Rescue of the United States Pharmacopoeia by Organized American Pharmacy in the 1870's.* American Journal of Pharmaceutical Education, 15 (1951), 172-184.

The Standardization of Pharmaceuticals

Burton, Clarence M., *History of Wayne County and the City of Detroit, Michigan,* Vol. 5, pp. 641-650. Chicago, Detroit, The S. J. Clarke Publishing Co., 1930.

Fink, Leon C., *Precedence in Standardization.* Unpublished manuscript, 1897.

Grier, James, *A History of Pharmacy.* London, The Pharmaceutical Press, 1937.

Lyons, A.B., *Manual of Practical Pharmaceutical Assaying.* Detroit, D. O. Haynes & Co., 1886.

Moeller, Josef, and Thoms, Hermann, *Der Real-Enzyklopädie der Gestamten Pharmazie,* Vol. 2. Berlin, 1908.

Parke, Davis & Company, *Complete Catalogue of the Products of the Laboratories.* Detroit, 1897.

Proceedings of the American Pharmaceutical Association, Vol. 50, p. 18, 1902.

Standardized Products. Parke, Davis & Company, Detroit, 1911.

Taylor, Frank O., *Forty-five Years of Manufacturing Pharmacy.* Journal of the American Pharmaceutical Association, Vol. 4, 1915.

Taylor, Frank O., *Parke, Davis & Company.* Industrial and Engineering Chemistry, October, 1927.

Taylor, Frank O., *Quality Control.* Journal of the American Pharmaceutical Association, Practical Pharmacy Edition, March, 1947.

They Made Drug Therapy Reliable. Therapeutic Notes, June, 1941, p. 184-189.

Wresting the Jungle's Secrets

New York Herald-Tribune, Nov. 20, 1940.

New York Times, Nov. 19, 1940.

Rusby, Henry H., *Jungle Memories.* New York, Whittlesey House, 1933.

Taylor, Frank O., *Forty-five Years of Manufacturing Pharmacy.* Journal of the American Pharmaceutical Association, Vol. 4, 1915.

Tschirch, Alexander, *Handbuch der Pharmakognosie,* Ed. 2. Leipzig, B. Tauchnitz, 1930.

Wimmer, Curt P., *The College of Pharmacy of the City of New York.* Baltimore, Read-Taylor, 1929.

Stanislas Limousin— Pharmacal Inventor

Goris, Albert, *Stanislas Limousin.* La Pharmacie Francaise, March-April, 1939.

Lechler, Harry P., *Cachets de Pain.* American Journal of Pharmacy, 48:100-102, 1876.

Weisinger, Mort, *The Fabulous House of Squibb.* Coronet magazine, Vol. 36, No. 5, pp. 64-68, Sept., 1954, Chicago.

Wimmer, Curt P., *The College of Pharmacy of the City of New York.* Baltimore, Read-Taylor, 1929.

Remington, Joseph Price, *Cachet de Pain or the New Method of Administering Nauseous or Disagreeable Powders.* Proceedings of the American Pharmaceutical Association, 23:614-616, 1875.

Zwick, G.A., *Medicine Wafers.* Proceedings of the American Pharmaceutical Association, Vol. 24, 462-464, 1876.

The Era of Biologicals

Antitoxin Kills Where It Should Cure. New York Journal, Dec. 12, 1897.

Bacteriological Products. Pharmacal Notes, Vol. 3, No. 4, 73-76, 1896.

Burton, Clarence M., *History of Wayne County and the City of Detroit, Michigan,* Vol. 5, pp. 641-650. Chicago, Detroit, The S. J. Clarke Publishing Co., 1930.

Diphtheria Antitoxin Now Furnished on Demand. Pharmacal Notes, Vol. 2, No. 2, 38, 1895.

Houghton, Elijah Mark, *Dr. Charles Thomas McClintock, a Memorial.* Bulletin of the Wayne County Medical Society, Detroit, 1921.

Houghton, Elijah Mark, *Memorandum,* August 9, 1898. Files of Parke, Davis & Co., Detroit.

Jenner, Edward, *An Inquiry into the Causes and Effects of the Variolae Vaccinae.* London. Printed for the author by Sampson Law, 1798.

Patent on Diphtheria Antitoxin. Western Druggist, Vol. 20, pp. 334-335, Aug., 1898.

Progress in Biologicals. Modern Pharmacy, Vol. 26, No. 1, 18-21, Feb., 1942.

Schlingeman, A.S., *The History of Bacteriology in Michigan.* Compiled for the 57th annual meeting of the Society of American Bacteriologists at Detroit, April 28-May 3, 1957.

Taylor, Frank O., *Forty-five Years of Manufacturing Pharmacy.* Journal of the American Pharmaceutical Association, Vol. 4, 1915.

The Development of Chemotherapy

Fourneau, Ernest (1872-1949). Annales de l'Institut Pasteur, 77:643-647, 1949.

Henry, T.A., *Ernest Fourneau, 1872-1949.* Journal of the Chemical Society, London, 1952, pt. 1, pp. 261-266.

Poggendorff, J.C., *Biographischliterarisches Handwörterbuch,* Bd. VI (1923-1931). II Teil (Verlag Chemie, Berlin, 1937), p. 786.

Pharmaceutical Research

Bockmüll, F., *Antipyretica und Analgetica der Pyrazolonreihe.* Medizin und Chemie, Bayer-Meister, 1933.

Ferchl, Fritz, *Geschichte der Pharmazie in Einer Stunde.* Stuttgart, 1951.

Griffith, Ivor, *Medicine in the Making.* The Trained Nurse and Hospital Review, 110: 177-179, March, 1943.

Kopp, H., *Geschichte der Chemie.* Leipzig, 1931.

Miescher, K., *Drugs in the Advance of Science.* Angewande Chemie, 65: 273-286, 1953.

Shryock, Richard H., *American Medical Research, Past and Present.* New York, Commonwealth Fund, 1947.

Pharmaceutical Manufacturing Comes of Age

Bulletin of the History of Medicine (various editions).

Burton, Clarence M., *History of Wayne County and the City of Detroit, Michigan,* Vol. 5, pp. 641-650. Chicago, Detroit, The S. J. Clarke Publishing Co., 1930.

Glover, John George, and Cornell, William Bouck, eds., *The Development of American Industries,* Ed. 2. New York, Prentice-Hall, 1951.

Oldest Drug Firms in U.S. American Druggist, Vol. 131, No. 3, p. 24, Jan. 31, 1955.

Taylor, Frank O., *Forty-five Years of Manufacturing Pharmacy.* Journal of the American Pharmaceutical Association, Vol. 4, 1915.

Taylor, Frank O., *Parke, Davis & Company.* Industrial and Engineering Chemistry, October, 1927.

Urdang, George, *Retail Pharmacy as the Nucleus of the Pharmaceutical Industry.* Supplement No. 3 to the Bulletin of the History of Medicine, Baltimore, pp. 325-346, 1944.

The Era of Antibiotics

Bender, G.A., *The Good Earth Takes Care of Its Own.* Modern Pharmacy, Vol. 34, No. 3, May, 1949.

Brunel, Jules, *Antibiosis from Pasteur to Fleming.* Journal of the History of Medicine and Allied Sciences, 6:287-301, 1951.

Fleming, Alexander, *On the Antibacterial Action of Cultures of a Penicillium, with Special Reference to their use in the Isolation of B. Influenzae.* British Journal of Experimental Pathology, 10:226-236, 1929.

Fulton, John F., *Introduction (to Antibiotics Number).* Journal of the History of Medicine and Allied Sciences, 6:281-286, 1951.

Klumpp, Theodore G., *Address of the President: Stepping Stones of Scientific Progress,* in Minutes of the Annual Meeting, 1956, (mimeograph). American Institute of the History of Pharmacy, Madison, Wisconsin, pp. 1-5, 1956.

Marti-Ibáñez, Felix, *Historical Perspectives of Antibiotics, Past and Present.* Antibiotics Annual, 1953-1954. New York, Medical Encyclopedia, Inc., 1953.

Marti-Ibáñez, Felix, *The Next Half Century in Antibiotic Medicine.* Antibiotics Annual, 1955-1956. New York, Medical Encyclopedia, Inc., 1956.

Waksman, Selman A., *Historical Background of Antibiotics.* Antibiotics Annual, 1954-1955. New York, Medical Encyclopedia, Inc., 1955.

Pharmacy Today and Tomorrow

Urdang, George, *Modern Pharmacy.* Modern Pharmacy, Vol. 31, No. 3, Nov., 1946.

INDEX

References in boldface indicate the text pages upon which the
person's biography or the pharmacy subject is covered in detail.

236